Ageless Skin

**A guide to treating
your skin from
nought to ninety**

kathleen birch

Ageless Skin: A guide to treating your skin from nought to ninety
© Copyright <<2023>>Kathleen Birch

For more information visit my website www.kathleenbirch.com

ISBN: 979-8-891-09116-0 (paperback)
ISBN: 979-8-891-09117-7 (ebook)

GET YOUR FREE GIFT!

To get the best experience with this book, I've found readers who download and use my guide are able to implement faster and take the next steps needed to improve their skin and remain consistently on their ageless skin journey.

Your Skin Journey Guide

You can get a copy by visiting:
www.kathleenbirch.com

Dedicated to my three children
They never touched earth
But will always light up heaven

My own skin challenges and those of my clients have taught me more about life than you could imagine. Are you brave enough to see what those skin challenges can teach you?

TABLE OF CONTENTS

Decade Four from 30 to 40 years old

Decade Five from 40 to 50 years old

Decade Six from 50 to 60 years old

Decade Seven from 60 to 70 years old

Decade Eight from 70 to 80 years old

Decade Nine from 80 to 90 years old

INTRODUCTION

I have worked all my life, either as an employee or running my own business. My career in the professional beauty industry was pretty secure. Hands-on work wouldn't be taken over by machines—machines don't do a very good job where personal touch is required. I love my work and even though I am approaching retirement age, I still can't see a time when I would not be doing treatments.

I hadn't counted on COVID-19 though. It never occurred to me that I would be shut down because of a virus. I don't think anyone could have imagined the impact this virus would have on the world.

So even though I'm dyslexic and doing anything with the written word—even reading—takes me forever, I want to share the information I have gained over the years with you. I might not be able to do treatments anymore, but I can write.

I tried teaching facials online, but that was just too depressing. My clients enjoyed it and said that it was helpful, but I just missed that intuitive feedback that I get from doing a one-on-one facial treatment. So, I thought the best way to teach how to look after your skin correctly was for me to put it into a book. The easiest way for me to write a book was to share what I learnt from my journey with my own skin, so here goes.

I divided the book into chapters corresponding with each decade of my life and what occurred at each stage with my skin. I'm sixty-six years old now, so this gives you a good long range from which to glean.

You can jump straight to your decade to see what is happening with your skin at that time. Also, I thought it would be easier as a reference book if you are a therapist who just wants some information on a particular problem with a client of a certain age.

You could read this book as a story of my life, in which case just read the first section of each chapter. If you want information on skin, read the second section in each decade. I introduced something to think about in each chapter regarding different aspects of the beauty profession. Lastly, I included a section as a workbook for your use if you would like to use this book as a lifelong learning tool. In that case, I encourage you to read all the way through, as this will be more helpful for you.

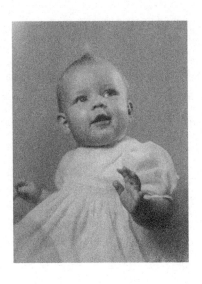

Decade One from 0 to 10 years old

BELIEVE IN YOURSELF AND YOUR SKIN

I was born on the twenty-fifth of January, 1955. This was a very special day—not just because I came into the world—but because it was the Chinese New Year.

I don't know if being born on a New Year is lucky or not, but Chinese horoscopes allot you a sign based on the year you are born. It's debatable whether I'm a goat or a horse.

Because the New Year is on my birthday, some horoscopes say I'm the year of the goat, others the horse. There does not seem to be a definitive rule to which I should be. I guess I could just pick whichever one suits me, but it would be interesting to know what I'm meant to be. So if anyone reading this knows how the rules work, please help me out.

This day is also special for Scottish people, because it's the poet Robbie Burns's birthday. I didn't realise that for a long while until I started organising parties for my birthday and kept hearing either, "Sorry we are at a Burns Night'" or "Are you going to do a Burns-themed party?"

One year we did a big fundraiser for the local surgery patients group. One of the doctors was from Scotland and had the idea of a Burns Night. Perhaps he was just missing home and thought this would be a great way to bring Scotland to London. Anyway, we did the whole thing— parading the haggis, Scottish dancing, and of course, reading Robbie Burns's work and toasting him with a wee dram of whisky. So much better to embrace what you are born with, don't you think?

Anyway back to all the reasons this day was special

You could say this date is special because I was Philip and Iris's firstborn. Also, the fact I was delivered into the world by two of my aunties makes it rather special too.

My mothers sisters, Ena and Nesta, were nurses in the army. They bought a nursing home just after the war. My mother's family are from Ireland. Buying a nursing home on the mainland at the suggestion of a colleague was quite a big deal, but it was a success.

My mother joined them to help with the cooking and cleaning, although she helped with the patients, too. In those days, it was "all hands on deck" so to speak.

My mother worked with my aunties at the nursing home for many years and she knew that when babies are born, they're not always that clean after coming through the birthing canal. When I was due to be born, she said to Auntie Ena, "Make sure the baby is washed first before you hand her to me."

Now, this is what really *makes it a special day—because, after all, this is a book on skin.*

As my mother knew only too well, a baby does not have the most beautiful skin when it's first born, never mind all the blood and stuff that my mother wanted washed off. The skin can look wrinkled and red, patchy and blotchy, and sometimes has bumps, dents, and birthmarks to name just the most common problems. But, when I was born, my auntie handed me straight to my mother saying, "She's absolutely perfect. She's as clean as a whistle! There is not a mark on her."

I've always put this down to the fact that my mum craved oranges throughout her pregnancy, Vitamin C is very good for the skin. Strangely enough, it's the one thing I'm not fond of eating now.

Even though I was perfectly clean, Mum still insisted I be washed before she would touch me. Did I subconsciously feel that rejection? Soon I was bathed and that all-important touch of skin-to-skin bonding between mother and baby was done.

The skin is our outward protection from the world. It gives us shape, but is also how we feel the outside world. It is the barrier to all that is outside the sphere of who we are inside. This amazing 3 mm keratin layer gives us our appearance, is the way we feel everything we come into contact with physically, and forms this special bond between mother and child. Of course, sound and smell are relevant, but *touch*, the feel of a mother's warmth and the soft touch of the baby's body are registered through the skin.

We know how important this touch is when babies are born prematurely, as my sister was. She was in an incubator for her first days during which touch was encouraged to keep her healthy and give her a fighting chance of survival.

Touch is one of the skin's jobs, but the skin has many more important jobs. I will go into more detail on how the skin works later. First, let's continue following the journey of my own skin as I grew into adulthood.

I was lucky enough to be born without any skin problems, and really for the first years of my life my skin was very good. My mother used a gentle baby soap and talc on all her children. We now know talc is not good to use, because it can be harmful to a baby's lungs if too much is inhaled. Fortunately, it never harmed my siblings or myself.

I had a pretty uneventful childhood. I was terribly shy, which people who know me now will find hard to believe. I used to hide behind my mother's skirts and was not at all sociable, in complete contrast to my sister Susan, who is only fifteen months younger than me. In fact, I used to think my parents mixed us up because Susan was much more outgoing and confident, far more like an older sister than a younger one. Everyone always thought she looked older than me, too.

I was a weedy little thing and it didn't help when I got tuberculosis in my appendix when I was young and stayed at the nursing home for quite a while before having the appendix removed.

I'm saying this like I have known about it for years, but if it wasn't for my sister doing reflexology on me in my thirties when we stayed in Ireland with my then-retired aunties, I probably would still think I had an appendix. Sue was doing my feet and, not for the first time, said to me, "I'm sure you must have had your appendix removed."

I retorted as always, "I think I'd know if it had been taken out. And where is the scar?"

Then, on this occasion, the voice of our auntie behind us said, "Yes, you did have your appendix removed when you were five years old. I always knew that surgeon did nice, neat work."

I always wondered why I was at the nursing home all that time. It suddenly came back to me as Auntie Nesta told us about the tuberculosis, that Susan had wanted to pull off a plaster on my tummy—typical of her wanting to be involved. When we looked closely, we found a small mark, but it was more like a chicken pox scar. It didn't look like any operation had been done there, and it could hardly be seen at all. The reason I spent that whole time at the nursing home was always described to Sue and me as "Kathleen having a *germ*."

I don't think even my mother knew all the facts, or knew how bad I really was. The aunties never liked to worry her

We used to go to Ireland every summer for our holidays, and I think that was very lucky for all our skins. Ireland is not known for its sundrenched beaches. It's called the Emerald Isles because it rains so much everything is lovely and green.

I was not fond of the beach. Hiding behind a wind breaker every time you went there just to be able to sit there in any kind of comfort seemed like a waste of time to me. Why would anyone want to sit on a beach anyway? I spent most of my time under a blanket, if I was lucky—or a towel if I was not—just to keep warm. And that was even when the sun was out, which was rare.

In contrast, Susan would be moving the towel back and forth like a yo-yo to try and get a bit of sun on her skin. But clouds raced across the Irish sky and the sun went in and out all the time. It was pointless to try to get tanned.

I hardly remember ever putting on sun lotion. The sun was never out long enough to burn us, and most sun creams back in those days were designed to encourage your skin to tan rather than protect it from the harmful rays.

Times have changed and so has the ozone layer, which is the earth's protection (and ours) from the radiation of the sun's rays. I will give more information about that in the following chapters, but for now, suffice it to say that our holidays back then did not cause me any skin problems that would come back to haunt me.

That cannot be said for most people's holidays though, especially if they are in gorgeous, far-flung places with constant sunshine. If you know this is the case, be especially mindful of the chapter on sun protection.

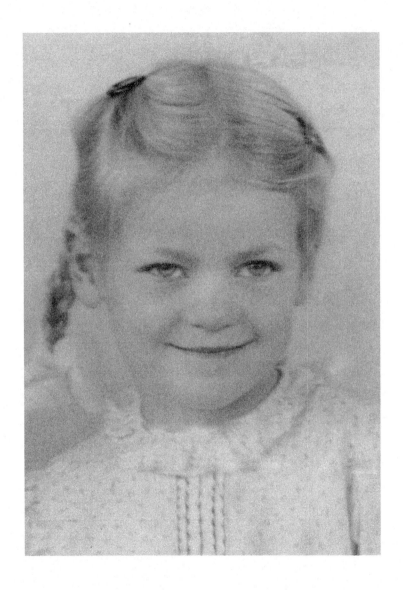

SKIN STRUCTURE

Most of us don't give our skin much thought. Did you know that it's the largest organ of the body? When we think of the body's organs we think of our heart, lungs, and all those things inside us, nicely protected by bones, muscle, fat, and guess what—the skin!

I think this is why it's not really thought of as an organ in its own right. Most organs in the body do a few jobs, the heart pumps blood around, the lungs put oxygen into our blood and draw toxins out. But our skin has loads of jobs, all without the protection that the other organs get, and as I said before, the skin is part of the other organs' protection, too.

Skin is very complex and has many things affecting it, internal and external atmospheres, emotions, diet, topical products, and lifestyle.

What we see is only the outer epidermal layer, the stratum corneum, but the skin is made up of five separate layers of the epidermis and these epidermal layers are all fed by the basal cell layer, which is where each epidermal cell—mostly keratinocytes—start their life.

Below the basal cell layer, which can also be called the dermal junction or stratum germinativum, is the dermis and below that the subcutaneous tissue or hypodermis which consists mostly of fat.

So what we call the skin, at its thickest part under our feet of only about 4–5 mm thick, is really a very thin layer of our body. In some places, it is no thicker than a sheet of paper.

I'm going to go into each individual job the skin does as we go through this book because I want you to realise what a huge impact we can have on each layer of the skin if it's not looked after properly, and how we can maintain and even improve the skin if we treat it correctly.

My focus in this chapter is a part of the skin that is rarely taught at school, and only really mentioned by skincare therapists. It's been given various names during my years in the beauty industry and is still not completely understood, but plays an important role in the health of the skin.

It's the protective acid mantle, or as it's called nowadays, the hydrolipidic film or layer, commonly called the natural defence barrier. It's a natural moisture layer that is made by the skin and is very delicate. It can be destroyed easily, but has the ability to replace itself very quickly or very slowly if the skin is not in good health.

Everytime you wash your skin, it is destroyed, and it takes a little while for it to replace itself. During that time your skin is more vulnerable to the outside elements and bacterial attack. I would like to point out that our skin has good and bad bacteria on it at all times. It's the ratio between the good and bad that is important. This ratio will mean the difference between spotty, unhealthy skin or not. I will go into comedones, spots, and acne in the next chapter.

For now let's concentrate on keeping the skin healthy. The first thing you can do is make sure your protective acid mantle is intact.

So how do we do that?

First you need to know how the protective acid mantle is formed, or think of its other name, hydrolipidic layer, which comes from *hydro* meaning water, and *lipid* meaning oil or fat, a layer, thin film over your outer skin cells (the stratum corneum). Yes, it is a combination of oil and water. Does this sound familiar? It's what you find as the basis of all moisturising creams.

The reason we use moisturising creams is to support this protective mantle, but it's a mistake to think that your over-the-counter cream is going to take the place of the acid mantle. That's because we need the natural elements that come from the combination of sebum (fat) from the sebaceous glands, sweat (water) from the sweat glands, and natural moisturising factor (oil) that comes up from the basal cell layer to make this protective layer. It also has to be the correct pH (hence its first name, acid mantle, with the natural pH of the skin as 4.5) so that it will have the best balance for good bacteria to thrive. Over the counter creams can help, but they will never take the place of a strong, healthy, natural protective acid mantle.

Skincare for babies and beyond

So let's start with you as a little baby. How should your mother have cared for your skin?

My motto is KISS, "keep it simple stupid," as my uncle George always used to say. I know we are not stupid, but KISS is still an appropriate reminder.

To be honest, I have realised over the years that the skin responds best at all times if things are kept simple. It's a complex enough system on its own without adding any more jobs for it to do.

So my advice is to bathe the baby gently with tepid water and dry thoroughly with a soft towel.

Babies do get skin rashes, but this is usually from the skin still building its immune system or a reaction to products. There are cases where internal factors from food can affect the skin, too, but in most cases it will clear over time if the skin is allowed to look after itself.

I would only add a gentle soap or cleanser once your child is moving around on its own, because it's more likely to touch things that could be ingested and cause harm, so an extra step of protection is needed then.

Your child's skin should not need a moisturising cream if they have a well balanced diet and the internal moisturising factors are healthy. If this is not the case and your child's skin is suffering, then a very gentle moisturiser can be used, but try and make sure that the cream has as few complex ingredients as possible.

Also, physical protection from direct sunlight is very important, not only for your baby's skin but for the baby's eyes, too, as the retina can be damaged by the direct sun's rays. I think physical protection is best when the baby is under a year old because all sun protection products have ingredients that may irritate immature skin, and I would never use any product that does not say it can be used on that particular aged child.

For these early years, on top of what I have said above, children need a well-balanced diet and good hydration. Both are essential to maintain good skin health. You will see that these two things do not change throughout our lives and will come up repeatedly throughout this book. What you put in the body's system maintains, helps, or hinders the system. It's simple to eat nourishing foods and not junk that uses up our precious energy and potentially harms the body or skin.

The other essentials are a good night's sleep, fresh air, exercise, and starting babies off on a good routine with these at an early age is important. This will help immensely as they grow older.

What is your daily skincare routine?

Let's get clear about the basics because what you do and how you look after your skin is the most important part of how your skin will fare as you get older. Of course, it also makes a difference in the way your skin looks today.

I would say that cleaning your skin and making sure it is protected are the basic requirements for your skin. Get these right, and your skin will stay in good condition. Anything else on top of this will be a bonus.

So how do you clean your skin?

You should start by asking why, because if you understood what I was saying earlier about our protective mantle and how important for our skin's protection it is to keep this intact, why would we want to disrupt this with cleaning? Everytime you clean your face you are losing that protection, so wouldn't it make sense to not clean the skin at all?

That is a good point. That is why I say that using any type of cleaning product should only be used on a baby after it starts moving around. As I said before, be cautious of what you use—as gentle a product as possible. That is what I am constantly trying to get across to clients who have overly cleansed their skin, causing problems because they have no protective barrier function from this over cleansing.

We need to clean our bodies regularly because if we do not, we might become rather smelly. This is not the case with our faces. The only real cleansing need is to remove any dirt from the day. If we have worn makeup, then it is imperative to remove that because a build up of stale makeup can cause all sorts of problems. It's never a good idea to go to sleep with your makeup on, especially for the sheets.

The most important time to clean your face thoroughly or do any kind of skin treatments is in the evening so your skin has time to recover its protective mantle during the night. In the morning, all you need to do is refresh your face before applying protection for the day and makeup, especially if it has protection in it, too.

Back in the 1970s when I did my training, using a cleanser and toner was drummed into us as the best way to look after your skin. Soap and water were frowned upon as not caring for your skin and being too drying. I agree with soap on the face being a little too harsh because most soap is very alkaline. Although it helps with cleansing, it destroys the skin's natural acid pH for protection. But for those smelly body parts, it's great.

Now we know that water is not the enemy it was once made out to be. Soaps have improved a lot, too, and quite a few now have a more neutral pH.

So with the dazzling array of cleansing products on the market, what should you use?

If you do not wear makeup, you only need a light cleanser to remove dirt. It can be a pH-balanced soap, wash-off cleanser, or eco-friendly cleaning mitt which does not require any cleansing product at all.

If you do wear makeup, you do need to use something that will dissolve or lift off the makeup.

If you use a product to dissolve the makeup, then you will need to correct the skin's pH with either a toner or water because to dissolve it usually requires an alkaline product. (See **Figure 1** below.)

Remember this thorough cleanse is done evenings only so the skin has longer in a safe environment to regain its acid mantle for protection. Remember, also, to make sure all cleaning products are removed so the protective mantle is quickly and easily regained.

Skin Cleaning	Pros	Cons
Water	No adverse ingredients Ph friendly.	Won't remove make up or dirt and grime.
Micro mitt Lift	No adverse ingredients, removes makeup, dirt and grime, Ph friendly. Eco friendly	Difficult removing waterproof mascara.
Soap and water Dissolve	Will remove dirt, grime and some make up.	Adverse ingredients, not PH friendly, won't remove oil based makeup, could irritate skin.
Wash off cleanser Dissolve	Will remove some make up, dirt and grime.	Adverse ingredients, may not be PH friendly, may not remove oil based makeup, could irritate skin.

Skin Cleaning	Pros	Cons
Oil or oil based cream cleanser Dissolve	Will remove makeup, but may require toner to correct PH and clear off skin.	Adverse ingredients, not PH friendly, could irritate skin.
Water based lotion cleanser Dissolve	Will remove some make up, but may require toner to correct PH and clear off skin.	Adverse ingredients, not PH friendly, could irritate skin.
Gel Cleanser Dissolve	Will remove some make up, but may require toner to correct PH or water to clear off skin.	Adverse ingredients, may not be PH friendly, could irritate skin.
Micellar water Dissolve	Will remove makeup, some dirt and grime, must be removed with water.	Adverse ingredients, not friendly PH, could irritate skin.
Cleansing wipes Dissolve	Quick but only removes some surface make up, and must be removed with water.	Adverse ingredients, not PH friendly, could irritate skin, won't remove make up or dirt and grime. Very eco unfriendly.
Eye makeup remover		
Water based	Removes most eye makeup, best for eyelash extensions.	Won't remove waterproof mascara.

Skin Cleaning	Pros	Cons
Oil Based	Removes eye makeup and waterproof mascara.	Can't be used before eyelash tinting and applying or using lash extensions.
Figure 1		

The next step is protection

As I said before, the main job of a moisturiser is to support the skin barrier protection, but some skins are more oily than others. The type of moisturiser is important to give your skin the correct balance of oil and water so that the skin barrier protection works correctly. If this balance is wrong, then our skin deteriorates and becomes unhealthy.

I'm sure you have all heard about our skin being described as normal, oily, or dry. Some skincare houses still use these categories, but we now know skin is a bit more complicated than that. There are plenty of other categories of creams, but I want to try and make this simple so that when you ask any company for a moisturiser you are asking for the right thing. And I'm talking about a basic moisturiser here, nothing more. I will go into all the other creams available as we go through the chapters on different ages.

Do you feel as if your skin has a good layer of oil on it? Let's put the question another way: is your skin shiny when you wake up or does it become shiny throughout the day, especially on the nose? Then it could be described as having enough oil, in which case you need a cream that does not add more oil but which is water based—that is, a cream when it is made has oil added to water. It is a more liquid lighter cream. It may be described as a lotion. So for a skin that already has high oils levels, a lighter, lotion-type moisturiser is required.

Does your skin feel like it lacks oil? In other words, it feels dry, possibly flaky, and feels tight after rinsing in water? Then your skin could be described as dry, in which case you need a cream that will add more oil to your skin and is an oil based cream—one when made has water added to oil and has a much richer and thicker consistency to it. It will be described as a cream or even a balm. So for a dry skin that has low levels of oil, a richer cream or balm moisturiser is required.

Getting this right is the first step in picking the right cream for your skin protection needs.

You need to bear in mind that the skin is constantly changing by replacing the skin cells on a regular basis and the atmosphere you are living in is also changing. I'm going to be talking about this in more detail later in the book, but for now, be aware that these constant changes inside and out will make a difference to which type of protection cream you need. So each time you are running out of cream, ask yourself, is this still the correct type of cream for me to be using? Are the answers to the above questions still the same? Or do I need to adjust my skin protection cream to a lighter lotion or heavier cream, depending on whether my skin is feeling oily or dry?

Now I can hear some of you saying, but my skin doesn't feel oily or dry. It's somewhere in the middle, or what could be called normal. I'm not a big fan of the word normal—it's all relative to what is considered normal in the circles where you find yourself. So for now, if you feel the answer is not yes to either of the above questions, then you fall in this middle band. Be thankful, because this means your skin has a good oil to water ratio and should be functioning well.

So for deciding on the correct skin protection cream, I would consider the outside elements you find yourself living in the majority of the time. If the atmosphere is dry, pick a thicker cream moisturiser, if the atmosphere is humid go for a lighter lotion moisturiser.

How did your life start?

You may like to use this book as your discovery journal. I'm guessing I don't have a load of genius babies reading this, so this first chapter is not where most people reading this will be in their life right now. Wow, it would be brilliant if you are under ten years old, because when you get to my age you will have just rocked life and look amazing—something not many people can do! You are either careful, correct, and look OK, or you blast through life not giving a damn and end up—if you manage to get to my age—looking like hell.

Wherever you are on the journey, let's course correct and learn from our past what works and what does not. Go forward with some amazing tools so you can have your cake and eat it, too.

So the first part on this journey is an excavation of what has occurred before.

Let's start, like me, on what was happening when you were born, your parents, the conditions in which you found yourself, country, social structure, religion, or lack of it. You get the picture of what we are looking for here—the pros and cons of how you started your life. Oh, you might say, those lucky ones that are born with a silver spoon in their mouths—but you will discover, if you don't know already, that this is rarely the case. Money is not everything, but it's true—it does help. As my darling husband loves to say, money is an enabler and should be treated as such, not the be all and end all of everything.

I've been very lucky because I was born into a very warm, open, and happy family. I mostly had security in my life emotionally, if not always financially, but this might not be the case for you.

What challenges do you think this has caused you? What did you learn from the situations you had to deal with? How might any of that affect your skin? Or any other part of your body?

You might have been born with a skin condition that impacted on your life right from the start. How did this make you feel? Did it limit what you thought you could do? Or did it become a guide to help you become stronger?

These are the things to take note of. Are there any insights or patterns occurring? Be aware of your early challenges as we go through the book and see if they keep repeating. Learn from this—an old pattern or life choice might need to be changed.

There may be another part of your body, if not the skin, that is guiding you with the challenges it keeps bringing up. Be open to this and substitute it where I am using the skin to help me.

As I said earlier, I was a very timid and shy little girl before I went to school. In the next chapters I will share with you how I overcame this, but also how I recognised resentment, anger, and other negative emotions that were holding me back. Looking back at what happened earlier helped me to realise that I was in these emotional states, and awareness of a situation is half the battle of overcoming it. Please do your homework, but remember that back then you were only a little child and didn't know any better. No beating yourself up now for something that was bad before—just look and learn.

One of the things that I had to learn, which was really not my fault, was knowing right from wrong. My auntie used to give me money and sweets, and she would say, "Don't tell your mother," or "Don't tell Susan. This is just for you." I always felt terribly guilty that I got this extra attention, and on one occasion it got even worse when Sue and I were going to the fair with my auntie. We went the wrong way, ending up walking along a towpath by the canal. I was on the water side and suddenly my aunt pulled me in, swapping us around saying to Sue, "Kathleen must stay safe, it doesn't matter if you go in." Neither of us could really swim properly at that age. I was mortified that she cared so little for Sue's safety. We were both scared, but this just made it worse.

We were taught by my parents to always play fairly, share things equally, and no one got more than anyone else, but here was my auntie breaking all the rules and giving me the impression this was acceptable. For a while I thought this was OK, but it was so confusing to know when it was or when it was not. I now know it was never OK, but this was before we even went to school. Adults were supposed to know better and teach us correctly right from wrong, but it's not always the case.

So if you have learnt some bad life lessons from adults when you were a child, forgive yourself, forgive the adult, and move on knowing that you know better now.

Decade Two from 10 to 20 years old

CULTIVATING GRATITUDE FOR A GOOD SKIN

The local school in the area where we lived was large and catered to all types of children from very mixed backgrounds. The classrooms were huge and if you were the shy retiring sort, as I was, then you could easily get lost in the system. My aunties recognised this problem and that I was struggling to keep up, especially as I had missed classes when I was not well. My father wanted us all to go to a private school because he recognised how important education is to get on in life, but he could only afford to pay for my two brothers, so my lovely aunties stepped in and paid for Sue and I to go to a good school.

In 1963, I went away to the School of St. Mary and St. Anne, Abbots Bromley in Staffordshire. It was a very high brow, Woodard school with strong religious ethics, for the education of young ladies. I was there from 1963 to 1972 and it worked wonders on me. I arrived as a timid little mouse and left able to hold my head up with as much confidence as I could muster—actually not that much I now know, but at the time and compared with how I was before, I felt like a giant.

I don't know how I managed to get accepted for boarding school at all because you have to take a special entrance exam to qualify for admittance, and I was dyslexic—although it was not recognised back then as it is today.

I remember looking at the question papers. It was the first time I'd even seen an exam paper and I thought it was all gobbledygook, but I must have got something down on the page that was OK because I managed to get into the school. It also helped my sister get in because I had passed.

We went together, joining St. Bridget, the lower school for juniors. We went together because it was thought it would help us with the transition of leaving home at such an early age, especially for Susan. We started in the summer term, so we were the only new girls because it was the last term of the year. I don't know why we didn't start in the autumn term like everybody else.

Susan loved it. She was like a fish in water. I hated it and tried to run away three times, not getting very far though because I had no idea which way to go once I got out of the front door.

My first school report said I was "completely overwhelmed by all the other girls."

And I think if I had not managed to settle in the next term, Mum and Dad would have been advised to take me away. Luckily for me, I started getting the hang of it. They realised that putting Sue and I in the same dormitory was a mistake, as things got better when we were split up.

I was given extra time because I was left handed. The dyslexia was not even recognised then. My mother was severely dyslexic, too, we now realise. You only have to look at her address book to see that she had no idea where to put somebody from an alphabetical order point of view. At school I was given extra time in my needlework exam because I was left-handed. The funny thing was that my teacher was also left-handed, so actually I had an advantage over everybody else in needlework because of that.

Even though I was held back academically by my dyslexia problem, I found a certain confidence in myself and part of this learning process was just acting "as if" I was confident.

You either sink or swim at boarding school and I wasn't very fond of the idea of drowning, so I started copying the things the most popular girls at school were doing and that moved me from being picked on or ignored, to becoming part of the gang. But it was an odd incident that actually made me realise the power of acting "as if."

People who know me will laugh when I say I will do almost anything for something yummy to eat. I know one friend who has used this ploy a lot because she knows I'm so very fond of my food.

At school the dining room had very large tables lined up on either side of the very large room. Next to this room were the kitchens where our meals came from and at the top end of the dining room was a small utility room where the crockery, water jugs, and condiments were kept. At the other end of the room was a large bay window where a smaller table sat and this is where the teachers who were not on duty ate. Teachers on duty sat one at each of our tables.

Each table had a plan, and the most senior girls sat closest to the teacher—but then had to make sure the teacher was looked after. No one was allowed to ask for anything to be passed to them. This was to teach us to make sure that everyone had what they needed and you also got what you needed. The food was not that great at school and the only way you could tell what kind of meat was on your plate was by the sauce that was on the table—even that was not always a sure bet!

I was always hungry, but discovered two things that helped get rid of my hunger pains. No one wanted to sit at the end of the table, because whoever sat there had to get up all the time to fetch the food, clear up the plates, and fetch the water. First, I discovered that if I went to fetch the food and was pleasant to the kitchen staff I would almost always get a bigger and better portion—great for the whole table, including me. I was always happy to collect the water because in the utility room they kept trays of sandwiches, which were for the teachers' afternoon tea break, something we never got—a break or a sandwich. I would check no one was looking and grab a few from each end of the tray so no one would realise any were missing, shove them in my pockets, and walk confidently out as if nothing happened. What joy to eat later on in the day when I got a bit peckish! But I learnt from this that if I did anything with enough confidence, I could usually get away with it. Confidence opened many doors, but also being nice to people paid dividends, and everyone prefers a friendly smile and a kind word. So slowly but surely, I was not only learning my lessons at school but was also learning how to get on in life. The best way to overcome shyness is to learn coping strategies, and boarding school was certainly teaching me that.

I didn't have bad skin when I was in my teens. I wasn't affected by hormonal spots because I was a slow developer. I think it was because I was so slim and I didn't get my monthly periods till after everyone else in my class at school, including my younger sister in the class below me. Even after getting my period, in retrospect, my skin was not as bad as I always thought it was. It's amazing how when we think about our skin, we tend to be very judgemental and build things up to be so much worse in our minds.

I wanted to be the same as everyone else, and all the other girls were using strong lotions to try and get rid of their spots, so I started using a toning lotion, too. At this age, we have no idea the damage that can be done just trying to fit in. This harsh treatment on my skin was disrupting my protective mantle and was slowly destroying my skin's health.

The next mistake from my skin's health point of view was when I left boarding school in 1972 and went to sixth form college. This was when I started to wear makeup. I only wore a small amount initially. I didn't really know what I was doing, but I do remember seeing a picture of a Estee Lauder model and thinking she had the same shaped eyes as I did. I was always very good at art, so I looked at how her makeup was applied from a light and shade point of view—the same way I was taught in art classes—and that's how I discovered that applying makeup could make a huge difference to your appearance. The only problem was I was still using that awful toning lotion, not realising it did not do a good job removing makeup either and was only making my poor skin worse.

I wanted to go to art college straight from school, but my father told me that I had to get straight As in my O Level results, and even though I managed that in my mocks I got too cocky thinking it was in the bag. It wasn't, so I ended up at sixth form college doing art A Level.

I didn't really enjoy sixth form college. It was such a contrast to the strict routine at boarding school where every single minute was supervised. At college you supervised yourself, and it seemed to me that going to the coffee shop or record store was a better use of time if no one was going to correct me. After the first year I realised that I was not going to get anywhere if I carried on like that. I managed to get through the first year exams purely on the knowledge I gained from boarding school's over-achieving ethics, but this was not going to get me any A Levels, and I was realising I wasn't really cut out for academia.

After that first year when I realised that this switch to a sixth form college wasn't for me, I didn't really know what I wanted to do. That's when my mother pointed out that I enjoyed art and biology, and beauty therapy combined both of those. I started looking into it. Most of the places where you could train were in London, so I applied for quite a few. Back then I don't remember there being government-funded college courses in beauty therapy. I think it was only possible to get a private education.

We visited the various private schools for my interviews. All these places required at least three O Levels, and they were very particular that you were the right candidate to go to the school—so much more thorough than the training requirements these days. I remember one teacher checking my hands to see if I had the correct hands for the job and another, one of the top places in Cadogan Street, the trainer asked which other places I was going to look at. I told her I still had to see Henlow Grange. She said if I qualified from Henlow to come back to her and she'd give me a job anytime.

When we drove up to Henlow Grange the decision was made immediately, especially with the other teacher's endorsement. Looking at this magnificent building ahead of me, it was a no-brainer. I now only had to impress Leida Costigan that I was the right candidate for the school.

Henlow Grange was the first ever health farm. Now we call them health spas, but I think they called them farms back then because Henlow Grange was a stately home with acres of grounds which would have been farmed on years ago. There were health clinics and spas in London where people went for treatments, but Henlow Grange was the first ever place where you actually stayed overnight and spent days there for treatments. The rich and famous would come for weeks, but the average punter stayed for just a weekend.

There were different levels of training going on at the Grange, as we all called it. I was one of sixteen students there. We all paid to be trained by Leida Costigan and our uniform was blue overalls. We mostly all lived in a little house called the Elms not far from the Grange, but still in Henlow village. The basement of this house had been turned into treatment rooms for teaching equipped with treatment couches, so we spent most of the time there until we reached a certain level—then we started working at the Grange. There were also girls doing apprenticeships—they wore pink overalls and were being trained by the qualified beauty therapists at the Grange. All the qualified therapists wore white overalls, so when a client came for a treatment they would know at what level the therapist was who was working on them.

Each senior beauty therapist had her own treatment room. She was in charge of an apprentice who helped do some of the treatments, and usually they had four to five clients for treatments. Students were allocated to a room working with that therapist for a week and she was in charge of everything the student did.

But students all had to learn the trade first at the Elms before we were allowed to work on clients at the Grange. I remember it being very scary the first week I worked there. We were only allowed to do manicures at first, then eventually moved on to pedicures, body treatments, and G5, before massage. You knew you were doing well when you were allowed to do a facial on the client.

There were treatment rooms for waxing and other specialty treatments. We each were sent to these treatment rooms to learn each aspect of beauty therapy and working with clients in a professional environment.

If Leida was not happy with something, we would get a phone call late at night to go and sort the problem out. We all had to participate in the exercises for the clients each morning before we started our day. It was vigorous training—very full on—and on top of all that, we were used for photo shoots, TV appearances, and entertaining journalists and celebrities.

I remember doing a pedicure on a very well known beauty editor while she was having a facial. I couldn't believe how awful her toe nails were—they were so long they were almost growing back in on themselves—perhaps she was so busy with her work she hadn't time to practise what she preached.

I eventually qualified in 1974 and completed my CIDESCO in 1975 after working at the Grange. Another student, Hazel, and I were asked to do a special teachers' training course, as we had the highest grades in our exams. So we went to Spain to do an intense teachers' training course with Leida Costigan and then returned to Henlow Grange to teach a year of students.

I always thought it was a shame we had not gained more work experience before doing the teaching. Then my sister decided to come and train there the second year, so I gave up because I didn't think this was a good combination for either one of us. It was a pity, because I would have liked to have continued with all I learnt in the first year, but Hazel and I must have done a good job because one of those students, Nicki Caro, became the beauty therapist to Princess Diana.

Hazel and I had accommodations at the health farm when we started teaching, but it became very clear that we were the ones always called upon to do any extra jobs after hours, so we decided that we would move out. We got an apartment at the top of a large house in Bedford, the home of one of the girls, Tania, who was doing an apprentice training at the Grange. I still didn't drive at this time, but Hazel had a car and would drive us to work. Often she stayed at her parents' home not far away, so then Tania and I had to get the bus to work.

Hazel and I took a trip to Yorkshire to see my family and had a night out with my sister meeting all the local boys—most of them were sons of my parents' friends that I'd known for years. Hazel seemed very impressed with one chap and we ended up going out on a double date with him and his friend, who I suspect really liked Hazel more than me. Unfortunately after a few more dates with him I ended up getting pregnant. This was not in my plans, and so both the pregnancy and the relationship had to be ended.

What a nightmare that whole incident was. I was so scared of anyone finding out because I was so embarrassed about what had happened. How could this happen to me? I had been so stupid taking that chance. I went to the doctor, determined to do anything possible to get myself out of this mess. She was lovely and could see how scared I was, not being a bit prepared for motherhood at this time. An appointment was made and off to the hospital I went. I was meant to have someone come and collect me, but they let me go home in a taxi after I convinced them I had someone back home to look after me. I can't remember telling anyone, except the father, what I was doing. I think he was quite relieved. I felt perfectly fine after the operation. I thought it was all a breeze so went back to work the next day. That was probably a mistake.

I now know that my childhood "germ" caused complications. That night I felt awful. I had the most terrible cramps, rather like the worst period ever—there was no way I was able to work the following day. I went back to the doctor, and she gave me some tablets, but I just seemed to get worse. I decided I needed some loving home care. I took a train to Yorkshire to my parents for Mum to look after me. I couldn't tell her what was really happening, and my poor mother thought I was just suffering from period pains. By this time I was bleeding with heavy clots and could not be far from the toilet.

Mum wanted me to see our family doctor, but that was too risky for me, so I got back on the train to Bedford—a horrendous journey—and collapsed on my bed back in the flat. My doctor gave me some other tablets and strict instructions to rest, which I realised I should do. Eventually I felt better and regained my strength.

I'm sure Tania and her mother knew there was something happening, but no one said anything, and I kept my secret to myself only telling my sister after Mum died.

HORMONES

At this stage in a person's life, between ten and twenty years of age, hormones are affecting our bodies and especially our skin. The sex hormones in both men and women are being stimulated during puberty to develop us for fertility. Part of this increase in hormonal balance affects our sebaceous glands which are found in the hair shaft of every hair on your body. The sebaceous gland produces an oily substance called sebum. I mentioned this in chapter one, if you remember? It's part of what makes up your skin's protective mantle. The only problem is, during puberty our hormones make the sebum become thicker and this disrupts the bacterial balance on the skin. This thicker sebum is like the nectar of the gods to the bad bacteria, so their population increases. The thicker sebum also clogs the shaft of the hair follicle and produces comedones (commonly referred to as blackheads) that can then lead to inflammation in the follicle. Inflammation in the follicle produces a papule or pustule (commonly referred to as a spot), a papule usually being a large, red sore lump and a pustule usually being a large yellow lump. The degrees of redness, yellowness, largeness, and soreness are all important in knowing how to deal with them, but more on that later.

Added to all that is happening naturally in the body, we tend to make the issue worse with what we do. Girls start using makeup to make themselves more attractive and cover any blemishes, and boys start shaving and are not always fastidious with their cleaning routines. Both girls and boys are being driven by their hormones emotionally, which can make the skin worse, because emotions affect the hormonal balance. So it's a vicious circle, all at a time when you want to look your very best to attract your soul mate!

I want to mention about plastics becoming more prevalent while I was in my teens and this affecting hormonal balance in the body. I don't think we understood back then what harm plastics would do to our bodies or the environment. We were introduced to microwaving food, grabbing something from the freezer which was usually in a plastic container, and then heating it up. It was a really quick and easy way to live, but how many harmful plastic molecules were being seeped into our food? Now we realise that these plastic particles are affecting our hormonal balance. I'm not surprised that so many couples are having fertility problems these days.

So we are all familiar with teenage acne and now know this is partly caused by over activity of the sebaceous glands brought on by the hormonal changes in the body. This upsets the bacterial balance on the skin, which in turn—with the added congestion in the hair follicles—causes blackheads (comedones) and spots (papules and pustules).

It was thought that P. acne bacteria or Cutibacterium, as it's now called, caused acne, but this particular bacteria is actually beneficial for forming the hydrolipidic film. It's when it gets suffocated in the hair follicle that it causes inflammation there, which is the beginning of your spot. To overcome this problem, most people clean their skin too much, trying to clear the oiliness, but actually what they're doing is making their skin worse by taking away that protective layer which helps the skin. A case study in 2016 Propionibacterium Acnes On Our Face shows that this bacteria is on our skin all the time. It's the balance of the bacteria that we have to correct, and a good skincare routine will help you do this.

I think it might be a good idea to explain the formation of a blackhead as this is usually the beginning of most spots, though some can come from irritation on the skin and conditions like rosacea. A blackhead is a blocked hair follicle. This blockage is caused by either too much sebum from over activity of the sebaceous gland which also produces sebum or from dead skin cells that add to the blockage and cause a plug. This plug of sebum and dead skin cells then gets oxygenated by the air, turns black, so hence your blackhead.

A dry older skin can also get blackheads, but this is usually only caused by the dead skin cells blocking the opening so the sebum cannot flow on the skin's surface to make that protective mantle—in turn, that makes the skin drier.

Blackheads from both causes can turn into spots. As I described above, it's the bacteria becoming suffocated by this excess buildup of sebum behind the plug that causes inflammation in the hair follicle and hence your spot.

It is very important to deal with a spot correctly. Different stages of the spot's development require different types of care. I talked about a spot being a papule or a pustule. In fact, a spot usually goes from papule to pustule, but we may not always be aware of it. Depending when we notice the spot, it may have taken all night to become that large, yellow, pussy-looking thing.

The rule of thumb is, never attempt to squeeze that awful looking yellow pus if it has any hint of redness around it. The skin is in battle to correct the imbalance it finds itself in, and the pus is actually the debris from this battle. If you try to squeeze any spot that is just red or has any hint of redness you will do more harm than good because you could cause the battle to implode on itself causing more spots in the process. If the spot is just pus and no redness whatsoever, it can be carefully dealt with—preferably by a skincare specialist, but I understand this cannot always be the perfect solution. So only ever attempt to squeeze that pus away with clean hands and a tissue to protect the skin from your nails. Do this at a time when you know your skin will have time to recover, not as you are about to go out for the day. Evening is ideal as your skin has all night to recover. Very gently allow the pus to escape, then apply a disinfection cream or lotion to protect against further infection. The skin will form a scab to further protect itself, and you should allow that scab to fall off naturally in its own time so the healing process is complete and there is no danger of scarring.

To be honest, it's better not to touch a spot at all, but I know the temptation is too great for some and I'd rather you know the correct way to do it. But I stress again, if it is red or has even a hint of red, leave it alone. The correct procedure here is apply a specialised spot removing cream or antibacterial cream to take down the inflammation, and don't touch it. Any type of touching will only irritate the skin more and prolong the inflammation, hence a larger, more awful-looking spot lasting for longer than necessary.

Skincare for teens

Clean your skin with a gentle cleanser in the evenings to take off makeup and dirt from the day, doing an exfoliating treatment regularly to help keep the hair follicles clear. Only do this in the evening so the skin's protective barrier has all night to repair itself. This is the time to use any needed medication, too.

In the mornings, lightly refresh the skin with just water. If your sebaceous problem is causing your skin to look shiny in the mornings when you wake up, even after cleaning thoroughly at night, then a cleanser could be used. But try to avoid this because the protective mantle will need time to replace itself and your skin is more vulnerable till it does. I would advise possibly using a toning lotion to correct the pH on the skin if a cleanser is used, as this will help restore the protective mantle faster. I have never been a big fan of toning lotions after my use of them back at school, though I think they have improved since then and most have a better pH balance.

Remember to give enough time to allow a new skincare regimen to work. Our skin replaces itself every fourteen to thirty days depending on how old you are, so you must give at least that amount of time to see if the skin improves before trying anything else. At the same time, be aware of how your skin is reacting and correct what you are doing if it does not improve after giving it sufficient time to respond. The rule usually is to give at least a third of the time that it took to produce the problem for it to heal, remembering that everyone is different and heals at their own pace. The worst thing you can do is keep swapping products each week. This will not allow enough time for a product to work and may cause the skin to become irritated. Of course, if your skin has an adverse reaction to a product, stop using it straight away, but don't replace it with something new at that point. Allow your skin to calm down and get back to health before trying another new product.

You have a skin problem, what do you do?

Here's a little bit about qualified skincare professionals. Who is the right person for the job?

I think it is even more complicated now than when I first started in the beauty industry as to who you should see to sort out your skincare problems. When I trained, it really was not that big an industry, more of a side show, focused on looking good.

Dermatology was considered the lower rung of the medical profession, and you only went into that if you couldn't hack it in anything else. A beauty therapist was someone who trained in all aspects of beauty, including a bit of hairdressing. (Lord help anyone who came to me for a haircut!) Finally, there were the people behind the counters of large department stores or pharmacies and that really was it.

Now it seems like anyone can become a qualified aesthetic practitioner (the catch all name for anyone in the beauty profession), even your dentist!

And hardly anyone is interested in natural skincare. It's all botox and fillers because that's where the big bucks can be made and instant results are guaranteed, but at what price?

Where does this leave you? Completely screwed, if I'm perfectly honest. The industry is not properly regulated and everyone is looking for the next big thing that will work miracles and make them a fortune.

That's not altogether a bad thing because it keeps driving the industry forward and continually innovating new products. But in some ways, I think we might have lost focus and need to get back to basic skincare. If that is done correctly throughout your life, there is more chance of you looking good in old age without the need for cosmetic enhancement.

Also bear in mind that cosmetic enhancement looks far better on a healthy skin than a decrepit uncared-for skin.

I have seen this firsthand. I had a client when I worked in Oxford who came to me regularly for facials. This would have been great if she had done any kind of skincare in between visits—I mean just cleaning her skin—but she did nothing. When I tried explaining I was only correcting the mess her skin was in from her doing nothing but piling on makeup, she said, "But that's why I come to you, because I don't have time to do anything and you make my skin feel so good." Eventually she decided that she was looking a bit old and needed a facelift. What a disaster—it just highlighted all the neglect of her skin. Even though she tried procedure after procedure, she lost that youthful glow a long time before the facelift, and surgery could never bring it back. If she had just done one thing, like cleaning off the makeup, it might not have been so bad.

In contrast, I had another client at that time who was older than my bad client. She also came for the same regular facials, but took my advice in between visits with a regular skin care regimen. She looked so much younger because her skin was well cared for and healthy.

I'm going slightly off track here because I really want you to understand who can help you and to what degree. I'm very keen for you to understand skin health—this will become clear as we go along.

If you are going to see someone to help you with your skincare, I want you to understand the strengths *and* limitations of each skincare professional. First, do you just want advice or do you need a problem solved? For advice, it is best to go to someone who understands how the skin works and how products will affect the skin. The person behind the counter will understand how the products they are selling work on the skin. However, they are limited because they may or may not understand the way the skin works, and they are not able to get close and personal to see your skin properly, especially as they are usually working in very artificial lighting. Be aware that the advice given here will be helpful for picking a nice cream, but will not solve a skincare problem.

The next level up is a beauty therapist, but you need to understand that beauty therapy has been broken down into smaller modules when taught. I have often heard someone describe themselves as a beauty therapist when they only have level one NVQ, which means they can do the basic hand, foot, and eye treatments, but have not done any skincare.

So be aware of how well qualified and how much experience the person has that you are going to see. A well qualified and experienced therapist will give good advice and in many cases can solve the problem, but should also know their limitations and when to refer you to another professional.

The next level up is the medical profession and seeing your doctor is an obvious choice, but your GP has to know so many more things, so they can direct you on to the correct consultant. With all the life threatening ailments we can get, skin concerns are very low down on the list, so their knowledge is mainly to recognize skin cancers and prescribe medication for any breakouts. But if you can get your doctor to send you to a dermatologist, you are more likely to get better results.

If your GP thinks the problem is too trivial to see a consultant, then it's better to go back to a well qualified and experienced beauty therapist to see what can be gained there.

I personally would not use a dentist, nurse, or any other person that has done a brief training in aesthetics for any skincare advice or treatment, including anti-ageing procedures.

If a person doesn't have experience in looking after the skin for at least five years, they should not be doing any kind of skin enhancement procedures, however medically qualified they are.

One of my doctor clients told me that out of all their years of medical training to become a doctor, the average amount of time learning about the skin is only one to two days.

A dermatologist is usually the most qualified for any skin care problem, but I have also come across dermatologists who are only interested in a quick fix and often resort to skin peeling to get that done. It's rather a harsh way to treat any skin. The epidermis is removed so newer, fresher skin cells are revealed, but often a client is not warned about how vulnerable their skin is after the procedure and the skin may stay that way for a long time. I had clients who went that route and were pleased with the initial result, but then had other problems particularly with pigmentation marks because the peel left their skin with less protection from the sun.

So there are pros and cons to all professionals and that's what I want you to be aware of for your own skin's sake. The best advice I can give you is if you are not sure about what someone said, always get a second opinion.

I had a client who came to me with skin that had been bad with papules and pustules, particularly on her chin, an area that often gets problems because it's related to the endocrine system (hormones) according to Chinese medicine.

The doctor gave her a cream to use and it had done a good job because the worst spots had cleared up. She occasionally got the odd one when her period was due, but that was not surprising. The trouble was she used this cream continuously to try and make sure no spots came. That caused the chin area to look a bit red and irritated, which by the way, can also cause more spots to come. The skin reacted negatively to the cream and sunlight on the cream irritated the skin more. I recommended cutting down using the cream and not to use it at all during the day, so any reaction to the sun was eliminated, but she'd still get the benefit of keeping the spots away. I then started her on a course of treatments to clear the redness, which in turn would help clear the spots. Once the skin was clear I told her not to use the cream at all—only apply a little at night if she could feel a spot coming—reducing the use of the cream further. The redness was beginning to go down too, and her skin looked much better. The reason I'm telling you this long-winded story is because it's important to realise the benefits and limitations to any medication. Unfortunately, doctors don't have time to tell you all the side effects. They rely on you reading the label, which may not give you enough information. I think this story highlights the need for caution when using medication because some medications can make the skin worse if not used correctly.

A doctor will usually start you off with a local medication cream if the problem does not look too bad. If it does appear serious, they mostly prescribe antibiotics before getting out the big gun Roaccutane. This is usually used as a last resort because of its side effects including dry peeling lips and skin. Not everyone will get all the side effects, but it's a long list and includes emotional trauma, too, so beware before going down this route. Roaccutane has been described as the only real cure for acne, and if you are unlucky enough to have this problem a short six-month course may be worth doing. But be aware that if the underlying problems remain, acne will come back and I know that it's quite normal for people to have to do a second or third course before it's finally gone.

A good skincare routine, healthy diet, hydration, exercise, and the correct amount of sleep are the best weapons for good skin, but when our hormones are out of balance—particularly due to puberty—we may have to resort to medication. Be sure to look at Decade Five on emotions to make sure they are not causing hormonal imbalance. It can also be a combination of physical and emotional, so you need to address both if you want your skin to clear and stay clear.

What's holding you back?

My dyslexia was becoming a real thorn in my side, mostly because I let it. I got into a panic doing any kind of exam or written word dictation and the more I panicked the worse it got. When we had to do TV appearances I tried to make sure I didn't have to say anything, so that's how I ended up on one of those machines to firm up your bottom. I was terrified I'd make a fool of myself if I had to speak and got my words mixed up. The fact that I looked like a bigger fool with my tiny little bottom on this massive belt didn't bother me at all—anything was better than having to speak in case I made a mistake.

Can you imagine how awful my end-of-year exams were? We had to stand in front of a panel of all our teachers plus a representative from CIDESCO. We entered individually and we were asked questions from the teachers on each different subject of beauty, chemistry, anatomy, and accounts, then we finished off with the CIDESCO representative asking general questions on all the different aspects of beauty therapy. I don't know how I got through that. It's amazing that I actually put myself through that at all, because what you think can happen often makes you too afraid to even try, and then stops you doing anything.

So what do you think has been stopping you from doing something you're afraid to do? Possibly, as in my case, it's the fear of looking like a fool or fear of just doing the thing in the first place. It can be a fear of failure or a fear of success, but whatever it is, it's stopping you from getting on with your life and living your life to the fullest.

I found that if I get out of my own way and just get on with something I've been putting off, maybe because it seems such a huge job, it's not as bad as I thought it was in the first place. Half the problem is that I've built it up to be something bigger in my head.

Anthony Robbins called this stacking. You saw one problem after another problem until you had such a big stack that it was completely weighing you down and you saw no way out. This huge stack was stopping you from getting started because you didn't know where to begin.

An example of that is doing my accounts. Because I'm self-employed, I have to hand my accounts in each year for assessment. I have an accountant to do the sums, but I have to put it all together for her. That's the bit that I put off, week after week until, of course, it becomes a much bigger job— not only because it all piles up, but in my head it becomes a mammoth task. Each week I hadn't done them raised the stack even higher. But I found if I broke it down into increments and then did those little steps often, I actually enjoyed doing it and got a great sense of satisfaction when it's done.

So whatever it is that is holding you back, first find the fear behind the problem. Is there something you can learn or do to overcome this? Perhaps you have made the problem into something bigger than it is by stacking and you need to break it down into smaller easier increments. One of my favourite sayings to help me remember this is, "How do you eat a frog? One bite at a time." Everytime I feel overwhelmed by something that seems too difficult I think of that saying. It makes me laugh, which already helps overcome the fear, then I look at ways to make the job easier by breaking it down into bite size pieces.

I hadn't let the pregnancy hold me back, but the anger and frustration with myself because of how negatively I perceived my dyslexia problem was eating away inside of me. You will learn in further chapters how your thoughts can alter your body's chemistry and end up showing on your skin or other areas of your body—sometimes with devastating effects. Don't let this happen to you.

If acne is holding you back, then go back over Decade Two on hormones, or perhaps it may be an emotional problem, so please continue reading.

Decade Three from 20 to 30 years old

HAVING SUNSENSE—OR JUST HAVING SOME SENSE

What had I done? This was the shock of my life. I really didn't realise what living on your own was like until I moved to Oxford. When I was in the flat in Bedford, Tania's mother was always inviting me for meals and looking after me. I became her second daughter. This was not the case in Oxford. A very nice lady rented me the room, but she was not interested in getting to know me, never mind cooking me a meal.

I lived in an area of Oxford called Summer Town, which I discovered was considered a very affluent place to be. It was a lovely double-aspect room and quite large, but I had to do all my cooking and eating in there, too. In one corner of the room there was a little camping stove, for want of a better word, to do my cooking. I was allowed a shelf in her fridge in the kitchen, but had to do all my washing up after my meals in the bathroom, taking in a little washing bowl which I put in the basin. This was a shock to me. I realised I had actually been living a life of luxury, also. I had never even cooked my own food. Occasionally, I had to do something for myself when I was in Bedford, but I was mostly looked after by other people.

I discovered the indoor market in Oxford, which is a really beautiful place to go food shopping. It tempted even the most reluctant person to want to try and cook. I managed to get my food from there and by reading recipe books, I eventually taught myself to cook. My mother was a fabulous cook—I really should have learnt from her. I may have picked up a little bit but not as much as I should have, and I guess having been at a boarding school from such a young age probably didn't help matters.

I had a job with Orlane, a French skincare and cosmetic company, in Debenhams in Oxford. I started a brand new beauty salon in a small room just off the hairdressing salon on the top floor. The hairdressing salon was a different company and handled all their own bookings from their reception, whereas my bookings were done by the Orlane counter down on the ground floor.

This proved to be a bit of a problem. It's not really the conventional way of doing bookings for salons, and in fact, this turned out to be its downfall.

Initially the salon did very well. I was building up new clients on a regular basis and increasing the amount taken in sales by the cosmetic counter. This was the prime purpose of the beauty room, and it was exceeding everyone's expectations, so everyone was very pleased with me. It started going downhill when the hairdressing salon realised they were missing a trick and wanted the room back again so they could hire their own beauty therapist. They saw how well I did. In fact, lots of their clients came to me for treatments because I chatted with them when I was not busy in the salon and told them about the different things that I did.

Because Orlane had signed a contract for a certain period of time, the hairdressing salon was not able to get the room back. Instead, they opened up a different room in which to do beauty. When clients called for an appointment, Debenhams switchboard would direct them to the wrong place, and defaulted to the hairdressing salon. People came to my room thinking they had an appointment with me, but they had been scheduled at the hairdresser's beauty salon. It was a mess and I got thoroughly fed up with it, so that's when I decided to look for another job.

My best friend Jenny had just joined a company called Coiffeur Transocean, who ran the hair and beauty salons on cruise liners, supplying them with hairdressers and beauty therapists. She was just about to join the ship she would be working on in the Caribbean.

That was the life for me! By the time she arrived on her ship, the Island Princess famed for the TV series, I already had my interview and was assigned to Royal Viking line which had three world class cruise liners. I was joining the Royal Viking Sea in Copenhagen. The ship was in the middle of its summer season doing two weekly cruises alternating the Fjords of Norway to the Nord Cap with the Baltic Sea cruise—my first taste of the communist Soviet Union as it was back then.

People would always tell me how lucky I was to work on a cruise liner, but I would say it was not luck that got the job, it was my merits. The lucky part was that my assigned ship travelled all around the world, whereas the ship Jenny was on only travelled around the Caribbean! I know many would say that's not bad, but I would rather join a ship in Copenhagen and from there go to every continent on the earth.

I remember when I first flew out to Copenhagen—it was my first flight out of the UK.

I had to spend the night there before I joined the ship. The company booked me into a hotel near the port, and as I got into bed that night under a duvet—the first time I'd ever slept under a duvet—thinking how strange this was. What was I doing in a strange country? I don't understand the language and I'm about to join a ship that I've got no idea what it's going to be like, and I know nobody on it. I didn't need to worry, and it was the only time I had second thoughts, because when I joined the ship the next day I was warmly greeted by all the other girls that worked in my department. I especially remember how lovely Lee was—she was the therapist whose place I was taking. She said when she joined the ships, nobody showed her what to do, so she was determined to make sure that she would show me the ropes.

The first place she took me was where I would be sleeping, a really small room with a porthole just above the sea line. Later I realised how lucky I was to have a porthole. Many crew on board the ship did not have any outside light at all. In this tiny room were two bunk beds. Underneath the bottom bunk was two drawers, one for each person, two small wardrobes—the sort of narrow tin thing that you see in gym changing rooms—were at the head of the bunks by the door and underneath the porthole at the bottom of the bunks was a bench seat with a table to one side. The opposite side of the bunk beds and by the door as you came in was a basin. There wasn't room to swing a cat, and I shared this with Josie, one of the hairdressers. This was to be my home for the next year.

I brought far too many clothes and completely the wrong things. There was nowhere to put them all. Luckily we were coming into Southampton in three months' time so I could offload the jumpers, coats, shoes, and boots I didn't need with my parents when they came to see me. One thing you realise when you live in such a small space is you don't need many clothes. Because we were mostly in hot places, we really only needed light-weight things. We had a uniform for work, so that cut down on the clothes needed, too.

Next Lee showed me where I would be working. I had a small area curtained off from the hairdressing salon which had four stations for each hairdresser. It was midship about three levels up from our cabin in the crew area.

It didn't have any natural light, but we were right beside one of the doors out onto the lower deck so it didn't feel too bad from that point of view. It was great when we were passing anything of interest, like going through the Panama Canal for example—we would quickly run out of the salon and not miss a thing.

Anyone who has been on a cruise liner lately will think it unbelievable that I was the only beauty therapist onboard and only had a curtained off area to do treatments.

When our whole family went on a cruise for my mother's eightieth birthday there was a whole floor dedicated to the spa, with at least ten beauty therapists, plus hairdressers and complementary therapists. How times have changed.

All the crew ate in the crew mess which had its own team of cooks, separate from the passengers. As the ship was registered in Scandinavia and most of the crew were from there, our meals had a very Scandinavian feel to them interspersed with Germanic continental because the chief chef was Austrian.

There were approximately twenty-five different nationalities onboard within the crew and the average age was twenty-five, too. Mostly Norwegian officers, sailors, and cabin staff; Italian, French and German waiters; the English did entertainment, photography, and personal care which we were part of; and there even was a Chinese laundry down below in the lowest part of the ship.

Lee explained how the booking system worked. When the ship was at sea, we all worked full hours, 9:00 a.m. till 6:00 p.m. with an hour lunch break, but when the ship was in port the hours were reduced to 10:00 a.m. till 4:00 p.m., also with an hour lunch break. On embarkation days we didn't do treatments, but spent the time doing bookings. Lee told me I'd be amazed at the line of ladies queuing to make their appointments on those days. Of course, this was all before the internet or even a good telephone system aboard ships—the only way to book was to be first in the queue.

There is no such thing as a normal work week on ships. The time was divided between being in port or at sea, so this meant having a day off was a bit of a challenge, especially for me. The hairdressers took it in turn having the quieter port days off because they didn't all need to work then. But as I was the only therapist, I had no one to take my place, so I came up with a good plan.

If I had bookings, I would work and if not, I'd have a day off. In reality, this meant I got most port days off, especially the good places. I'd tell the passengers they didn't want to miss out on this wonderful part of the world having a treatment, and I'd make sure I fit them in when we were at sea. This also meant that I was very busy at sea and rarely got a lunch hour or finished at 6:00 p.m., but it was worth it.

In India I was determined to see the Taj Mahal in Agra. Dad had told me of his trip there when he lived in India and of spitting from one of the turrets—charming I know, but a typical joke for my Dad and I wanted to do it, too. The ship came into what was then called Bombay, now Mumbai, not exactly that close to Agra—two flights away as it turned out. Marianne, one of the hairdressers I now shared a cabin with, and I went straight to a travel agent as soon as we were allowed off the ship to organise our transport. Quite a feat seeing as we only had three days to do the round trip. We flew from Bombay to Delhi that afternoon, but our flight from Delhi to Agra was not until 2:00 a.m. We had hoped to be able to stay in the hotel rooms available at the airport in Delhi, but they were all booked up—not surprisingly at such short notice. So we joined all the other people who couldn't afford or couldn't get a room, sleeping on the seats in departures. We arrived in Agra at 5:00 a.m. and hired a driver for the day. We then went straight to see the sunrise over the Taj Mahal. It was an amazing sight—the beautiful white marble shifting from grey to gold as the sun shone upon it. After a simple breakfast we drove out to see the old fort before spending the afternoon at the Taj again before our flight back. As mentioned before, I love my food, especially curry. Unfortunately, I had eaten something very bad in Manilla in the Philippines. I had been unwell for days, so I took dried biscuits with me. This was my dinner instead of the authentic curry I was hoping for. It was too risky enjoying curry and then suffering Montezuma's revenge again.

It was only when doing repeat cruises like the Baltic Sea and coast of Norway that I had to work in port time.

All the crew sunbathed on the aft deck nearly every moment we got the chance. Everyone seemed to have the most amazing tans, but with my pale Celtic skin I never really got any colour at all. I remember complimenting one of the Norwegian stewardess on her beautiful chocolate tan saying I wish I would go that colour. She replied, "But you are a lovely colour of cream."

I had a three-month break before I joined the sister ship Royal Viking Sky in Los Angeles, USA.

It was during that time I discovered that my younger brother David was gay. This was not really a surprise for me, but after discovering what it was like to live with a load of gays on the ship and seeing all the shenanigans going on there, I was concerned. He had always been a bit odd with his attitude, and when he brought a so-called girlfriend around I could tell it was not really a proper girlfriend relationship.

My concern was nothing compared to my Dad's reaction. He took it very badly, as if it was an affront to his manliness, and just kept telling anyone who wanted to hear or not about his gay son. Eventually Mum told Dad how stupid he was being, and that it was no one's business but David's what his sexuality was.

Thank goodness my Dad listened to Mum and realised he was only making matters worse for himself and David. He got over it, but it took a long while for him to come to terms with it.

I still had good skin, but *I* didn't think it was good skin. It was really only my nose that was a bit congested and bad.

SUN AND YOUR SKIN TONE

I think this is one of the most important sections in the book as far as natural anti-ageing is concerned. If you look after your skin, keeping it healthy with good skincare, balanced diet, fluids, exercise, and sleep, it will all help with anti-ageing. But if you want to keep your skin looking good for years to come, the most important thing is to keep your face out of the sun. That goes for the rest of your body, too, if you don't want to have to cover up to hide the wrinkles and pigmentation as you get older. I saw many examples of badly sun-damaged skin while I was working on the ships with all those elderly ladies who had sunbathed all their lives not realising it made them look older. Now they had leathery looking faces, pigmentation marks, and crepey, sagging skin on their bodies.

The sun causes more damage to the skin than anything else, and the worst problem about it is that you don't see the damage straight away. You will, of course, see the redness and feel the burn when you have been out in the sun for too long, but this is mostly superficial compared to what the sun is doing deeper down. The sun penetrates down to the dermal junction with the basal cell layer where our new skin cells are formed and affects the DNA of the skin cells. But it's not until later in our lives that this damage to the DNA can be seen on the skin, usually as solar keratosis which can be little or large dry scaly patches, either natural skin colour or darkly pigmented. Either way, they don't look great on the skin. I can tell you that from personal experience, plus all the ones I have seen on my clients. If you are unlucky, especially if you have the red hair gene, these can then turn into one of the many forms of skin cancer, none of which you want to get—especially malignant melanomas which can be fatal.

I know this all from personal experience. It was at this time in my life when I got skin cancer, but it was quite sometime later that it was diagnosed. More about that time in my life later. Now I would rather we concentrate on keeping you safe and protected from the sun.

We need the sun for vitamin D production in our bodies, and vitamin D is very important for the immune system, something we discovered more about during the COVID-19 pandemic. One of the reasons that black people were more likely to get the worst symptoms of COVID-19 was because the extra melanin in their skins blocked the body's ability to produce vitamin D

The sun's rays have different lengths—the longer lengths penetrate deeper into the skin and affect the basal cell layer and so can cause premature ageing, while the shorter rays can cause more immediate damage because they are the ones that burn our skin. We've always been taught to keep out of the sun during midday. This is very good advice to make sure we don't burn, but if we want to stop our skin from ageing, we need to make sure we avoid the longer length rays, too. These rays are present first thing in the morning and late in the afternoon, just the times I used to sunbathe, thinking I was keeping my skin safe.

Now it gets a bit tricky. We've got to have a bit of sun for vitamin D, but we have to avoid the sun because it can burn us and can make our skin age. Another factor is knowing your skin tone, because that makes a difference in how much sun you are able to endure.

There is something called the Fitzpatrick scale which is a measurement of how much sun your skin can tolerate. It was developed by dermatologist Thomas B. Fitzpatrick when he realised that the amount of melanin in the skin determined how much sun your skin tolerated before it burned.

I have typical Celtic skin which is Fitzpatrick 1, the lowest tolerance on the scale. This means my skin burns easily and is more susceptible to skin cancer.

Take a look at the scale (See **Figure 2**) and see where you think you may be. If you're unsure, you can be tested to determine your Fitzpatrick number.

These are the things to know prior to talking about sun protection creams and what sun factor (the scale used for the protection level in the sun cream) to use.

The first thing you need to know about sun factors is that there are both UVA and UVB rays. UVA are the long rays I was talking about earlier that age the skin. UVB are the rays that will burn the skin and are typically found at midday. So the sun factor you need to use should take both UVA and UVB protection into consideration.

Hopefully you've determined your Fitzpatrick number, but I strongly recommend you see a therapist who does Fitzpatrick testing to make sure you are correct because this is so very important for skin health and longevity.

Fitzpatrick chart showing 6 skin types (classification) and 6 different skin colours, and respective reaction (burn time) to sun exposure.

Fitzpatrick skin Classification & Ethnic Origin	Typical Characteristic	Burn Time
Type 1: Celtic, English Northern European	Very white/fair skin. Blond hair, Blue, green eyes	Always burns, freckles, never tans
Type 2: Nordic [1-2] Ashkenazi Jewish Native American [including Inuit]	White, fair skin. Sandy to brown hair. Blue, green, brown eyes.	Usually burns, freckles, tans with difficulty.
Type 3: Jewish, Central Eastern European, Southern European Mediterranean, Maori NZ	Fair to olive skin. Brown hair, Green, brown eyes	Sometimes burns, but will tan.
Type 4: Chinese, Korean, Japanese, Thai, Vietnamese, Filipino, Polynesian, Central/South American Indian. Indian.	Olive to light-medium skin. Brown hair. Brown eyes.	Rarely burns
Type 5: East-West African Eritrea & Ethiopian, North African, Middle East Arabic Dark brown skin	Black hair, Brown - dark brown eyes .	Very rarely burns
Type 6:	Black skin, Black hair Dark brown - black eyes	Almost never burns .

Figure 2 *from Advanced Skin Analysis, Florence Barrett-Hill*

How do you pick the correct sun protection?

If your skin is red and already burnt, the damage is done. You want to make sure it does not actually look red. My sister and I used to press our skin and if the skin marked and came up red very quickly, we used this as a guide that we had enough sun—not very scientific, but better than burning.

Let's use this example: if you were in the sun with no protection and your skin was red after ten minutes, to double the amount of time you can be in the sun without burning, you need to make sure you have a sun protection factor (SPF) of at least 20. It should be applied thirty minutes prior to being in the sun and then reapplied just before going in the sun to give the longer lasting protection.

Now you would think that the higher the SPF the longer you will be protected, but I'm sorry to say this is not the case, and every time you reapply your sunscreen you are only getting half the amount of protection as the first time it's applied.

The other thing to take into consideration is what you're going to do in the sun. If you are at the beach and are going in the water, you need to make sure that your cream is waterproof so you are still protected in the water where UV rays are multiplied due to the reflective factor of the water. Even if the cream is waterproof, I still advise people to put another layer of cream on after they have dried off. Also bear in mind that if you sweat, your protection will be reduced due to the SPF being thinned from both the sweat and the sun itself as the cream dries on the skin.

It's important to put the correct amount of cream on your skin and to make sure you have covered every area of skin that is exposed to the sun. Don't forget your ears, they always seem to end up getting burnt. If the cream is not applied liberally you will not get full protection, and anywhere it may be rubbed off should be reapplied frequently.

The NHS website recommends two teaspoons of cream for face and neck and two tablespoons for the body with a swimsuit on. I personally think more is best, but this is a good guideline.

If you have a sensitive skin, then take into account that the higher the SPF the more chemicals that are in it. These chemicals can cause more sensitivity on the skin. In this case I advise avoiding the sun altogether, but I give more advice on skin sensitivity in the future decades.

Skincare for twenties

Some twenty year olds may still be affected by hormonal acne, in which case, stick with the skincare rules in the previous chapter. This is the time we begin noticing our skin is not bouncing back from a late night out as well as it used to. We may see an effect from alcohol on our skin—the dehydration in our bodies from alcohol affects the skin, too, and this dehydration will appear on the skin as fine lines that, with age, will not disappear as we hydrate again.

These are self-induced wrinkles, not ones caused by expressions that we use Botox to try and prevent (more on the use of Botox later). These fine lines can be prevented by selfcare, keeping a good diet, drinking water, sufficient sleep, exercise, and reducing self-abuse—for example bingeing on alcohol.

Our skincare regimen is as before—cleansing and protection.

But if you are clear of puberty and your hormones have settled down, skin cell reproduction begins to slow down. Believe it or not, we are now beginning to age. Hopefully you are not seeing more than the faintest fine lines around the eyes, but it's now that you should begin an anti-ageing regimen.

Begin with some extra care like exfoliating in the evenings and maybe adding a hydrating mask. If the skin is dry, use the appropriate serum plus night cream if needed, depending on the amount of dryness. A home-care evening once a week or if you are able, a professional facial treatment will be very beneficial for your skin in the long run against skin ageing.

The morning routine should be refreshing the skin and applying moisturiser to protect the skin, plus sun protection, either incorporated in your moisturiser or foundation. Now is the time to use sun protection daily if you want to look good in years to come. What your parents did to protect you from the sun is important, too, because the earlier you have sun damage the worse the problem as you age. You are old enough now to be responsible for yourself and prevent any early sun damage becoming worse or even mitigating it completely.

Are you prepared for opportunities?

As I said earlier, I was always told how lucky I was working on cruise liners, and I answered it was not luck but my merits that got me the job. Being prepared to take the opportunity when it presents itself is so important. That can require taking a risk or a leap of faith. Are you brave enough to do that? Luck is great, but you only become lucky if you are ready and open to receiving that luck. What I mean is that even while you don't feel very lucky and things are not going your way, you still have to show up every day, put in the work, and get the experience and qualifications so you are prepared for that lucky break when it presents itself.

I have discovered over the years that being lucky is a state of mind, too. If you think you are lucky, you will be. And if you think you are not, that will come to pass, too. Whatever state of mind you put out is usually what comes back to you, so bear that in mind.

I worked hard to get my qualifications, I had a good interview, I presented myself well so they would accept me for the job, and more importantly I was prepared to take the risk of joining a ship where I knew no one or what it was like or how I was going to be treated—all far away from home so not easy to return to if it didn't turn out so well.

I wasn't always good at taking opportunities. I remember a time later on in my life when I decided it would be a good idea to open a male-only salon—unheard of at that time.

Because of my Aquarius insight, I'm already a little bit ahead of time with my ideas. This seemed like a good opportunity, and I was right. If I had opened then, I'd have really cashed in on the male market. But I remember someone telling me I'd only get the gay guys coming, and that would put off anybody else. What they didn't realise is where the gays go, everyone else follows—as I discovered in an episode of *Sex in the City*.

I didn't take that risk. Do I regret it? Yes and no—it's not really a regret, but it would have been interesting to see that path taken and how it would have turned out. Remember you can never make a wrong decision, it's just teaching you a different way of doing things. Regrets are only when we're uncomfortable with the outcome of the decisions we've made. If you are uncomfortable, then course correct and start sailing in another direction. Don't ever leave yourself with regrets. It's never too late to change your mind or learn something new. Who'd have thought this dyslexic child would be writing a book in her sixties!

What have you overcome or have to overcome?

I'd managed to overcome the main setbacks of my dyslexia. I recognised that the more I panicked about it, the worse it got. If I stayed calm and didn't try to rush things, I would normally get through reading something and get the correct meaning of it—very helpful when taking exams to understand the question. Then you have a much better chance of giving the right answer!

I thought I did a really good job but now, dear reader, looking back I realise I was only at the first stage. I feel like a completely different person now compared to what I was then.

We are all on a journey of discovery—discovery about who we are, what we are here to do, and what lessons have to be learnt on the way. What have you learnt so far?

I learnt that staying calm and not becoming like a headless chicken trying to do too much at once really helped me to not become overwhelmed. Then I got far more done in the long run.

I think we are given challenges throughout our lives to help us grow and make us stronger. We can learn from these challenges and improve our lives or just let them overcome us and get dragged down by them. What have you had to overcome? What did you learn from that? How has that made you stronger? Has it taught you more skill sets? Has it changed the direction of your life?

Maybe you are in the middle of one of those challenges right now. Don't let it get you down. Look for the lessons it's trying to teach you. You will come through this. When you feel you are at your lowest ebb, this is usually when the tide turns and things begin to improve.

Shyness and dyslexia were only the beginning for me. I had far more challenges to overcome, but getting over those first obstacles on my path gave me the courage and the know-how to face what was to come and help me succeed. I have always been a glass half-full kind of person. Being positive in the face of adversity helps you to find a way out of it.

At this time in my life I started looking into meditation. When I was younger, we had holidays over in Ireland staying with my family. I was always intrigued by my auntie Nesta going off to read the Bible in her room. When I sneaked a peak during those times, she just looked like she was asleep. I eventually dared to ask what she was doing and was told she was meditating on the Bible. I had no idea what this meant and dismissed it at the time, but it was there in the background of my thoughts. As I got older I wanted to find out more about this mysterious thing called meditation that could help keep you calm. Staying calm was something I realised already was valuable, and while I was on the ships I put this to good use.

Our working hours in the salon while the ship was at sea were 9:00 a.m. till 6:00 p.m. The only problem with this was that the ship's mess for the crew stopped serving food at 6:00 p.m., too. We never finished spot-on, invariably running late because a client hadn't turned up on time, so we had this constant problem in getting an evening meal. We would take turns going down there and bringing plates of food back up to the salon. They weren't happy about that, but they let us do it—until they made a rule that no plates could be taken from the crew mess. What were we to do now? We ended up having this big argument each night. It was my turn to face the music—try and get us some food. As I ran down to get there before 6:00 p.m. I was thinking to myself, *Here we go again. There surely must be a better way.* As I got in line to collect the food I just breathed deeply and asked for guidance from whatever power would help. My turn came. I made the usual request and got the same negative answer. Instead of going into our usual rigmarole of how unfair the system was and what were we expected to do, I just stood there quietly, then asked, "Do you have any silver foil?" I think she was as shocked as I was at this request. She, of course, was expecting the usual banter, but she just said, "I'll go and see." It just popped into my head, if we can't take plates, maybe we can put the food into silver foil to take back to the salon. This would keep our food hotter, too. And that's how we solved the food problem. By keeping calm and expecting the best, I came up with an answer that did the trick.

This became a main skill in my tool box and something I will share more about in the following decades.

Always stay inquisitive. If something intrigues you or you don't understand, try and find out more—you never know where it may lead. We are meant to keep learning and growing. I don't think we ever stop. That is part of the fun of life if you stay open to change. It's inevitable, and nothing stays static. Remember the lesson about skin replacing itself continually throughout your life—you are not the same person from one moment to the next. Embrace this, use this. Things can only get better if you open yourself to that possibility. Allow yourself to overcome and learn.

BE KIND TO YOUR SKIN, YOURSELF, AND OTHERS

It was not like real life working on cruise liners. Everything was done for you when it came to everyday living, rather like living in a hotel. Eventually you have to get back to reality. I loved working on the ships, but I knew it was time to come back down to earth. It wasn't easy because life on the ships felt like a continuous holiday with every day being in some sun-drenched exotic place. Even though there was a bit of hard work thrown in, it was a charmed way to live. I should have learnt from that because really that's all life is.

You have to work to afford to have fun, but it's good to have fun at work—and that makes a lovely life.

My skin got a bit of colour from being continually in the sun while I was on the ships. It would be going too far to call it a tan! I didn't realise the damage I was doing to my skin. I felt and looked good, but underneath the surface of the skin, the sun had already affected the DNA of my skin cells.

Originally I went to work at Elm Farm Clinic in the Cotswolds to help out a friend of my sister. Her parents had opened a clinic for her. They were short of staff, so that's how I came to work there on a temporary basis. I really enjoyed it and ended up staying a couple of years rather than just the two weeks I was meant to be there. It was so beautiful, doing treatments and looking out on fields with cows and sheep—such a pretty place to be.

It's here that I met my good friend Tish. We shared a house together. In the winter it was so cold that the toilet water froze over. I had a Mini in those days—my first car, bought with savings from the ship, and I'd only just passed my driving test. I used to have to park my car on a hill. Because of the cold, the battery on the car always went flat and I'd have to jump start it by rolling it down the hill. In fact, that became the normal way of starting it, but that little car was the only car to manage to get up Burford Hill when it was full of snow.

That Christmas was very cold and icy. I planned to drive back to Yorkshire on the evening before Christmas Eve, but because of the weather my mother suggested I wait until the morning when it would be better to go in daylight. The next morning, even more snow had come down, but I set off anyway wanting to be home for Christmas. Despite the snow and black ice and everyone else at the bottom telling me it was impossible, I managed to get up that hill. But the black ice got me in the end. I nearly ended up in a ditch on the first skid. I managed to keep the motor running, thank God, so I was able to continue on my way, but on the second skid my car did a circle, ending up facing the opposite way on the road. The engine stopped and wouldn't start. I had to knock on people's doors to ask for some jump leads. Eventually I got it going and was once again on the road to home.

Tish and I used to talk about when we were eventually married. We reached that time of life when we wanted to settle down with a boyfriend. We talked about having children or what we would do instead if we couldn't have children. It never occurred to me that children would not be in my future because I'd already been pregnant once—why wouldn't I again?

I remember a client coming for a treatment, so excited because she was pregnant for the first time—she was forty years old. I'm embarrassed to say I didn't realise what a big deal this was and I'd like to apologise to her now if she ever reads this book. I just said how lovely and carried on with the treatment. It was only later in my life that I realised how much this would have meant to her. The significance of that situation would come back to haunt me.

All my friends seem to be moving to London, even Tish, and when she left I thought I better go there, too. The boyfriend I had at the time had also moved from Yorkshire to London.

It's a rather funny little story about how I ended up in Chiswick. I was going to visit my sister in the summer and she worked in a salon called Flambards in Sheffield. They told me at reception that she'd already left for the day. A lady at the desk wanted a cab called for her, so I asked her where she wanted to go. "To Millhouses," she said. "The only reason I'm taking a taxi is because I'm bringing home this painting and I didn't want to take it on the bus."

I offered, "Can I give you a lift? I'm going to Dore and passing Millhouses on the way." She was very grateful and accepted, but on the journey there she started trying to sell me insurance. I said, "I'm very sorry but I'm so busy trying to find somewhere to live in London that I haven't got time to think of insurance."

"Oh," she said, "I might be able to help you with that. I have a friend, Alan, who lives in Chiswick. He's an actor and travels a lot with his work, so he likes to have somebody in the house. I'll get in touch with him and see if he needs anybody at the moment." Well, as luck would have it, he did!

When I went to look at the house, I fell in love with the area straight away. It was on Ernest Gardens just one minute's walk from the River Thames and Strand on the Green with all the lovely pubs along there. Now it sounds idyllic, but it was also right beside a railway line. It turned out the railway wasn't the problem—planes going overhead were far more noisy. But this was the perfect place to live in London when you're a newcomer from the country, and best of all, it was very cheap so when I eventually did move from there, I ended up buying my own place.

I had a job with a company called Violet Adair in Kensington at the top of Gloucester Road. It was a very smart hairdressing salon on the ground floor and below were the beauty rooms. It was on a self-employed basis so if you didn't work you had no money, and because I was the newcomer it took a little while to be able to build my clientele. It was hard work and really only when the other girls were booked up did I manage to get any clients initially.

Thank goodness my room at Alan's was so cheap. He really only wanted someone to occupy the house and keep it clean when he was away. He never did any cleaning himself, not even his own room. I gave that a quick hoover when he was gone.

I remember one Christmas my mother gave me a Christmas cake. Alan was away that Christmas and his friend Mac was staying in the house. When I came downstairs one morning I noticed Santa had lost his nose on the Christmas cake. I wondered why Mac would eat just a little bit of icing. Every time I looked at the Christmas cake another bit was missing. Eventually I confronted Mac and it turned out it was not him at all—we had mice! This was my first encounter with mice. I was horrified. It wasn't long after that that I started looking for my own place.

I had just changed jobs and was now working for Revlon with a much better wage. I joined as a make-up artist for their other skincare line, Ultimate II, based in Selfridges Oxford Street W1.

They moved me to different stores when needed for promotions, mostly to Harrods Knightsbridge. I used to do makeovers for magazines and newspapers.

I loved it and was promoted steadily from makeup artist up to manager of all four of the stations that Revlon had in Selfridges with over twenty staff to manage.

One of the girls at the counter inspired me to buy my own flat. She had just bought a lovely two-bedroom flat with central heating in Tooting Bec. for £25,000. I went to have a look as there was another flat for sale next to hers, but when I saw the area in the daylight I decided I'd rather stay in Chiswick.

I was earning a decent wage and could afford a mortgage, but needed a deposit to get a mortgage—so I had an idea. I asked my father if when I got married, would he pay for my wedding. Dad said of course, so I asked,

"Please can I have the money now to put down on my new place so I can get a mortgage?" My dad, who is a fairly astute businessman, loved this idea although he was not so keen on just handing over the money. It came with a proviso that when I married I had to give the money back. That is how I managed to buy my first flat—a tiny little basement flat with one bedroom, no heat, and needing a damp proof course—but it only cost £27,000 and it was in Chiswick.

I have fond memories of that garden flat. When I first moved in I had big ideas about how I wanted my flat, but very little resources to do it. Luckily for me, my brother David needed somewhere to live. He agreed to pay me a bit of rent to sleep on the sofa bed in the lounge. Now I could afford to sort out the layout of the flat and decorate it, after doing a damp proof course and putting central heating in— all with the help of my family.

David was a great cook. He had been working as a chef at a restaurant in Piccadilly Circus, so we had loads of dinner parties with friends and family. It was during one of these get-togethers that David got really upset and told me his big secret. Susan had been advising David to be careful with all this AIDS stuff. David suddenly got up and walked out of the room, so I went after him. He told me it was too late—he was already HIV positive. I had no idea what he was talking about and just tried to calm him down. He said I was not to tell anyone about this, so I promised I would not. He calmed down and came back to the meal. So there I was with this secret that I did not really understand.

Now remember, dear reader, this was before Google and the internet. We only had a massive block of a cell phone which did calls—badly—but certainly did not give information.

I decided to go see my doctor and ask him what HIV meant, the implications this had for David, and what I could do to help. Unfortunately, the lovely lady doctor I had when I first joined the practice had gone back to her home town in Scotland. I was transferred to another doctor. He was fairly elderly, but I don't think that was an excuse to treat me like he did. When I asked what HIV was, he said it was because David was gay and the promiscuous lifestyle he was living was why he was HIV. He did not tell me what HIV was—only lectured me on what David should be doing to correct this so-called lifestyle that was clearly in the doctor's head and had nothing to do with David, because how could it? He didn't even know my brother, nor anything about his life. I came away no wiser and very upset. I suspect in retrospect that he actually didn't know the answer to that question either. AIDS was so new then, and there was so much ignorance around it. I eventually got the answers I needed from London Lighthouse, a sanctuary for people living with HIV and AIDS.

I must say I took great pleasure in telling them why I was changing to another doctor's practice because I had no faith in the competence of my doctor.

It was at my flat warming party that I first met my husband. Apparently at the party I snubbed Andy. So he thought I wasn't interested and ended up with my best friend Jenny. It was only when we met again at another friend's house that we realised we should get together. His opening line was definitely a winner because he said he would help me with DIY on the flat, and he turned out to be very good. Our relationship developed from there and we were married in 1987.

Would I have married him if I'd known what was to come? We had the most beautiful wedding and initially we had a beautiful life. I was still working for Revlon, but was now the account manager in Selfridges, in charge of four counters and approximately twenty girls. I enjoyed the work and even though I wasn't doing treatments, it was very interesting and I learnt a lot about stock control and product ranges, which became very useful when I started my own business later. We sold my little garden flat to get a larger flat in the Grove Park area of Chiswick. That way I was able to pay my father back, so he could afford our wedding.

Soon after that my sister announced she was pregnant with her first child, and a few months later I discovered I was pregnant, too. Now pregnancy can make you do some very strange things. It's the hormones, of course, that tend to affect our judgement.

Unfortunately, Andy had lost his driving licence, but he needed to be able to drive for his work. For some strange reason, I thought it was a good idea to pack my job in and become his driver. Now I realise how stupid that was—not only because I was missing out on any maternity pay, but being with Andy 24/7, as any wife knows, can cause all kinds of disputes. I think the pregnancy hormones don't help your driving much either. Well, that's my excuse for some of the rather strange things I was now doing.

Susan told me she got these strange cramps when she was out at a restaurant during her pregnancy, so when I started getting cramps I thought it was quite normal. We went to Yorkshire for Christmas and I started getting some cramps that made me have to lie on the bed. Sue said hers were nothing like mine and I should go get checked out, so when we got back home I went to see the doctor. He then sent me for an ultrasound. It was odd, because I was still pregnant, but they could see nothing in my womb. I then had to go in for an investigation, at first just a biopsy, in and out in no time, but then they decided to look inside.

Poor Andy. He had seen me perfectly okay for all the first procedures, but when he came to visit at the hospital for the last procedure, he was shocked to find me monitored with machines in every direction. It was suspected that I had an ectopic pregnancy. I had never heard of ectopic pregnancies and had no idea what it meant or how life threatening it could be. All I knew was that I was very uncomfortable with all these machines, and they were doing an operation the next day so no dinner for me that evening—the worst thing ever for this lady who loves her food.

It turned out that the pregnancy was high up in the fallopian tube and they were unable to remove it without damaging the tube, so now I only had one fallopian tube left. That's all you need to get pregnant again so no problem—except that when I did get pregnant again (all before Susan gave birth to Charlotte) it was another ectopic pregnancy.

I remember going through the same symptoms as before and a nurse telling me not to worry as I'd probably only had a miscarriage and could get pregnant again. I went home devastated and really cross with the nurse. I'd told her, "I think you will find I'm still pregnant." Sure enough, they called me an hour later telling me to come straight into the hospital. I was so upset with the nurse from earlier that I told them I'd just eaten so they couldn't operate on me that night. I would come in first thing in the morning. That was stupid really—I was putting my own life in danger by not going in.

Remember, it's not clever to cut off your nose to spite your face!

But I was so indignant at how flippantly I had been treated that I never thought about the danger to myself. Would they have been able to save my other fallopian tube if I'd not been so cavalier?

I don't really think it made much difference in the eventual outcome, which was both fallopian tubes lost and no chance of getting pregnant naturally again.

Susan gave birth to Charlotte in July. I lost two babies in the time she had one.

Who would have thought it? There was no problem getting pregnant—only a problem with the baby developing in the right place. Apparently, it's very unusual to have two ectopic pregnancies. My sister was furious that no one had thought to check my second fallopian tube before I got pregnant again. No one had mentioned this was a possibility. Of course as you know, dear reader, it was reflexology that revealed me having tuberculosis as a child, the likely cause of the ectopics. Whenever anyone asked me about having my appendix removed, I always answered no. I was unaware myself till that trip to Ireland long after this. So even if they had looked into it further, would the outcome have been any different? Who's to say? There is no point wondering what could have been or would have been—it's better to just get on with what is.

That was my first disaster and not a great outcome for our marriage either. How awful it was having all our friends telling us of their new babies being born, when our only chance was to go through an IVF program.

We began on that journey, more hospital appointments, more tests, more disappointments.

This was not what Andy signed up for when we got married. It was not really his problem, so I think he must have just thought, *Let's do a trade in.* Before I knew it, I was discovering his illicit girlfriends all over the place. I remember confronting one, his physiotherapist, at Charing Cross Hospital. She had no idea he was married. He couldn't believe what I had done, how dare I go there and tell her I was his wife! This whole situation was getting very toxic.

My sister came down to visit. She said she now knew what people meant when they said, "You could cut the air with a knife." She could hardly believe how bad the atmosphere was in our home.

There had been a fairly regular stream of letters coming from Australia. Everytime I asked about them, Andy told me they were from his friend, also called Andy, who had immigrated out there, but I never got to see the letters. He made up some story about what was in them, so I decided to see for myself and grabbed the next letter as it came through the letterbox before Andy got to see it. I remember thinking as I opened it that I would feel pretty stupid if it was from

Aussie Andy, but that was wishful thinking. My suspicions were confirmed, so I just flushed the letter down the loo.

Eventually Andy decided to go to Australia to think about things. That's what he told me—rather a long way to go to think—but I knew one of these girlfriends had gone back there, and he was actually running after her.

While all these things were occurring in my life, my brother David was going through his own hell, too. He had been living in Spain with his Spanish partner Mariano. Rather like me, all was wonderful to start with. David was picking up the language really well, had a job, and they were living in the country with two rescue dogs and a cat. Then Mariano began getting sick with full-blown AIDS, so poor David became the main breadwinner and caregiver. This must have been horrendous for David seeing Mariano getting worse and worse, even more so because he knew this would eventually be his fate, too.

My mother went to visit David when she and Dad were on holiday in Spain. She took a train all the way from Alicante to Madrid on her own—amazing as I think about it now, because she was not known for such bravery. She used to ask me if David had AIDS. I was not lying when I said no, but I'm so glad she never asked about HIV.

Mariano passed away quite quickly after transitioning into AIDS. I can't imagine how awful this was for my brother having to deal with this loss, the funeral, and then moving to a smaller place in Madrid because he couldn't afford to keep their home in the country.

I visited him in Madrid after Andy left. We both needed a shoulder to cry on, but I think David had broader shoulders than me, because it felt like he was looking after me rather than the other way around. He spoke Spanish fluently now. I didn't speak a word so I relied on him a lot for getting around. The whole ectopic pregnancy thing and Andy's behaviour had taken its toll, plus keeping David's secret for so long didn't help the strain I was enduring.

But following Mariano's death, David allowed me to tell Susan and my other brother Peter about his condition. I did not feel quite so alone with this heavy burden and had someone else to talk to about it and ask for their advice, too.

I'm so glad David finally told my parents, although he told Dad first. Dad didn't want Mum to worry so said not to tell her—now we know where all this "not telling" people came from.

David moved back to the UK when the doctors said he had transitioned into AIDS. I was mostly taking care of him, but his apartment was in Cambridge Circus, so not that close to Chiswick, but at least in those days you could drive and park in town more easily. He always seemed to have a crisis when he was in East London, ending up in a hospital over there. It was so difficult getting there and never knowing if this was the slippery slope down, with him maybe being there till the end. That was the worst of AIDS back then—you never knew when your death sentence would come, or what would finally finish you off. The medication that now treats it had not been discovered then. You may not have the best quality of life, but at least you are here to see another day.

Anyway after yet another of these crises I told David it was time to be taken care of by Mum. He was reluctant because he knew it was going to be very difficult and emotional—it was like admitting that he was coming to the end of his life. But he agreed to be put on a train to Yorkshire. We said goodbye and I said I would be up to visit soon, but I never saw him again. He was home for a while with all the family, but then went into the hospital where he passed away peacefully.

These episodes in my life seem like a massive span of time. It's hard to believe it all happened in one decade. When I was putting this book together I was convinced that when David died it came closer to the end of the next decade. I was about to put it in with the next disaster that came a decade after that. I was so surprised when my sister told me David died 18th October, 1994. If he'd been alive today, his next birthday would be his sixtieth. I just can't imagine that. The beauty of dying young is that you will always remain young in everyone's minds. Maybe it's because he is always near me and pops into my mind every now and then, especially when I see a funny little annoying fly—mostly when I am doing massage—flitting around my head. *Hello David*, I'll think. *What's up in your world?* Then I carry on with whatever it is I'm doing.

All this emotional turmoil was playing havoc with my skin. This was the worst my skin had ever been. I was probably not looking after myself or my skin very well during this time. Also my skin got blotchy and red every time I cried and took hours to recover. This should have been a warning sign to me about a skin condition called rosacea, but back at this time it was not very well understood and still referred to as acne rosacea.

PRODUCTS

The products we use on our skin on a daily basis have a huge impact on our skin's appearance. You need to know what determines the correct choice of product. Please don't rely on the person behind the product counter. They may have some skincare knowledge and will probably know the range of products they are selling very well, but they are limited by what they see. They may see you with makeup hiding what is really going on with your skin or even without makeup in the artificial light, it is difficult to judge a skin correctly. I know because I have worked in those stores. I really missed my magnifier, the time needed to ask questions, and seeing how the skin reacted as I did a facial treatment.

And don't get me started on buying products online relying on just a marketing person's description on what the product will do.

So let's look at how the skin works so you can understand for yourself what type of product you need and are better able to judge when something is good or bad for your skin.

As I stated previously, the skin replaces itself every fourteen to thirty days depending on how old you are. It's faster when you are younger, slowing down as you get older and that's why skin seems to get duller as you age. The good news is that whatever the problem is, it can be history very quickly because of the wonderful way the skin works. The bad news is that if you are not looking after your skin correctly and don't correct whatever has caused the problem in the first place, the skin will keep churning out replicas of the same old damaged skin cells.

Our skin produces new skin cells (keratin) at the basal cell layer (epidermal junction). They start out all new, fresh, and juicy, rising to the surface, changing as they go through different layers of the skin till eventually on the surface they become flat, dry and loose. Then in time, they fall off. This is happening to your skin continuously. We are not really aware of it except when the skin has become compromised by a problem and this cycle is disrupted, as with conditions like psoriasis or eczema—the first does not shed skin cells correctly, the latter sheds too much, and both become itchy and sore. There are a lot of other extreme conditions of the skin, but for the time being I'll just stick with the more common ones.

Now you can see why I say you are not the same person you were even a day ago because this is happening throughout your body—each part is continually changing—either renewing or deteriorating depending on how you are caring for yourself. This is why we need to exercise to keep our muscles strong and our cardiovascular system working well. It's why we need to get a good night's sleep to help the renewal process and why we need to eat a good balanced diet to encourage healthy renewal of all the cells in our body, not just the skin.

I hope you can also see why skin has taught me so much. Learning about how it works and the way it constantly changes has made me used to the idea that our lives are constantly changing. We just have to accept this, even embrace it, so we don't get stuck in a rut.

With this information in mind, you can see why the products you use have to change, particularly as we go through different seasons which affect the skin and how it copes.

So bearing in mind that the skin cell passes through different stages as it rises to the surface, let's take a look at these stages and how we can help the skin cell look great even as it's about to fall off.

The most important thing, of course, is that the outer layer over the epidermis (the stratum corneum) is maintaining a healthy acid mantle. This will also improve if you are doing the correct care throughout the skin cell journey. It's a bit of a catch twenty-two situation—one helps the other or vice versa. In the same way, one will affect the other and vice versa if you are not caring for it properly.

So starting at the bottom and working up to that outer layer we look at the epidermal junction or basal cell layer. For a good strong basal cell layer, it's imperative that you eat the correct nourishing foods to support the cells. These cells must be well hydrated for correct cell function. A good night's sleep will give your body time to regenerate, as well as the skin. And there are facial treatments like the Hydradermie, which target this area to support it.

Most over-the-counter products will not affect this part of the skin directly. A serum is the only product that will penetrate the skin layers as it's designed to be drawn down into the epidermis, but as far as I know, it does not reach the basal cell layer. Only a facial treatment will affect that.

There was a program on TV that created an uproar about self care products in general. The presenter went around seeing what worked and what did not—except it was not a level playing field as the program only scientifically tested products sold in Boots and from nowhere else. So this and how she explained her conclusions without giving all the facts became a bone of contention for me. She said that only serums made any noticeable difference at anti-ageing on her skin and that the science backed it up.

I had no problem with that and agreed wholeheartedly, but what really got my back up was because she never explained how they worked and how to use them. Using a serum on its own may not be enough because it gives no protection for the surface of the skin. I had client after client coming to me and complaining that they bought this Boots serum and their skin was getting worse! I then had to teach how it was meant to be used, explaining it should always be used with a moisturiser over the top during the day, but could be used on its own at night if your skin wasn't too dry. Otherwise adding a night cream on top was necessary.

Eventually Boots brought out an advert explaining exactly that. They also must have had unhappy customers.

The next layers must be kept well hydrated to function correctly and thrive. There are enzyme functions that will not happen if there is not sufficient water in the skin cells so the cells and skin health will be compromised because of this.

This is why I continuously promote being well hydrated, so bear in mind if you have a night out with lots of alcohol, which dehydrates you, or are a regular consumer of coffee and tea which are both diuretics and make your body lose water, then you need to replenish it.

The other way we can maintain good hydration levels in the skin is the moisturiser we use, which is designed to slow down transepidermal water loss (TEWL), which is the natural process of water movement from the dermis to the skin's surface. It is accelerated by a warm, dry environment or slowed down by a cool, humid environment. These different environments will determine which type of moisturiser you should use, oil in water which is normally described as a lotion, or water in oil, which is a cream. Another way to explain this difference in moisturisers is how light, watery, and how quickly it appears to absorb into the skin—lotion or thick, greasy, and less absorbent into the skin—cream.

This is why we should consider a different moisturiser when we go away on holiday because of the different climate we may find ourselves in. This is also why we should use a lighter lotion during summer and a heavier cream as we come into winter.

As I said earlier, the rate at which our skin cells go from basal cell to stratum corneum slows as we get older. This makes the appearance of the skin duller and drier, so another important part of any skin care routine is exfoliation. For the time being, I'm only going to talk about products you can use at home, but there are many salon treatments to help this process and I'll explain more about these in a later chapter on anti-ageing.

There are physical exfoliants and chemical exfoliants. The first uses something abrasive to help sluff off the dead skin cells. It is fine on most skin types, and feels like something is happening when you use it, but should not be used if you have sensitive skin or you have rosacea or compromised skin. The latter uses the skin's ability to desquamate, which means it loosens the skin cells so they come off naturally and it accelerates this process. It doesn't feel like much is happening, but is ideal for those skin types that cannot use a physical exfoliant and you will see in time the skin looking fresher and brighter.

Exfoliants should only be used in the evening when you are not going out again so your skin has all night to recover its protective mantle, which of course will be removed along with the dead skin cells.

How often you use an exfoliant will depend on your age. If you are younger, once a week is the most you need to do, whereas older skins may require more than once a week. If your skin is fine and delicate with a thin epidermal layer, a more Celtic skin type, you need to avoid the aggressive physical exfoliant and use a gentle biological one. Keep exfoliating to a minimum, which would be once a month when younger and no more than once a week when older. A thicker, fuller epidermal layer, a more Mediterranean skin type, can usually take the physical exfoliant weekly, but more often as you get older.

Skincare for thirties

If you haven't already started on an anti-ageing regimen then this is the time that you may notice a few lines and think it would be a good idea. As I said earlier, we actually begin to age as soon as we have finished puberty, so ideally that is the time to start.

The first step is aiding skin cell replacement by encouraging it with a regular evening exfoliation. This will keep the skin looking fresh, too. So if you are not doing that already, I encourage you to begin. One thing I find helpful in keeping things simple is using a cleaning mitt, because the action of these also gives a very gentle exfoliation as you clean your face. I have found that I can get away with less exfoliating creams because of this. It saves time and money on products.

An anti-ageing serum that helps firm the skin is beneficial to add at night or under day protection because the skin begins to lose its volume at this stage of our lives. A serum that supports collagen and elastin production—your skin's framework—will help with the volume and keep the skin stronger for longer. But remember that if you have allowed the sun to damage your skin, these products will be limited in what they can achieve. Serums can only support healthy cells, sun-damaged cells may look less severe, but it's far better not to be in that position.

How does menstruation affect our skin?

Women have periods or the curse or whatever you want to call that awful, bloody monthly discharge that we get as soon as we hit puberty. Men don't realise how lucky they are not having this disruption each month that we have for nearly half of our lives.

I always had an issue with my periods. I didn't start them till my late teens, which was a blessing in some ways, but when I did they were never straightforward. I always got period pains a few days before it started and throughout the whole period, which would last up to a week and sometimes longer. This meant that almost half of a month was taken up with this hateful inconvenience. I managed my pain with painkillers, and I was in my thirties when I realised that I was addicted to the pills. I needed to take more and more pills to be able to get rid of the pain. It was only when one of the girls at the Revlon counter saw me taking the pills and told me that amount would knock her out if she took them that I realised I had a problem.

I looked into other ways to control the pain and what could be the underlying cause, because this was not normal for most women with their periods. I almost got a handle on it when I discovered I was entering perimenopause. That was even worse—almost a continuous period, with flooding and goodness knows what else. I was so thankful when I eventually stopped and never got another period.

But the lesson here for you is that suffering with periods is not the norm, and if you have been suffering month to month in a daze of period drama and pain, then please go and see a hormone specialist about it. We are not here on earth to suffer. I really wish I realised that many years ago. So much of my life was wasted dealing with this drama each month. Also, this has an effect on your skin. We know that our hormones affect the sebaceous flow, and if this is out of balance our skin suffers. Don't just put up with this each month. Get it corrected. You will be so pleased when you have a period without the drama—you will wonder why you put up with it for so long.

It is very likely that you will get a few spots on your skin just before a period, usually around the chin area. This is the area that Chinese medicine says is affected by our hormones, and of course periods are all about the drop in oestrogen that makes the womb lining clear itself.

If you are getting spots along the jawline this is more likely to be from stress than hormonal. Stress can be physical or emotional, so make sure you take that into account when dealing with the issue.

I have covered how to deal with spots in Decade Two under Hormones so go back and reread if you are still uncertain.

We get similar problems during menopause, but I will tell you more about that in Decade Seven when I explain about ageing. We should always deal with the problem at hand. There's no point worrying about what may happen in the future, because this moment of this day is the only time you can realistically make any difference in your life. Always stay in the present moment so the universal power will be present in you.

What has been your disaster?

So this is going to sound very strange, but all these awful events were the best thing to happen to me. Of course at the time I did not think that, and my poor sister would testify to the millions of phone calls she had from me, in tears, trying to work out what I had done wrong to cause all these disastrous things to happen to me. I was mortified that I was about to become a divorcee. Only my auntie Jessie had been divorced and everyone said, "Poor thing. It was because her first husband drowned and she never got over it." But I didn't have that excuse. I suppose two ectopic pregnancies could count as being pretty devastating, but as far as I was concerned being separated from my husband was far worse than anything else on the planet. To me, it meant I was a complete failure. The stigma of not being able to hold a relationship together was very strong in our family. Everyone else was successful, apart from poor Auntie Jessie, and I didn't want to be poor anything!

So how do we turn our worst nightmares into the dreams we'd rather have? First, we have to recognise that these challenges are here to make us stronger. We have to learn all we can from them. I learnt that when I got married I turned into a timid little mouse again. I thought that was the way I was supposed to be. Andy married this person who owned her own flat, had a powerful position within Revlon, earned a good wage, and had a lovely little Mini, with an electric sunroof, to zip around in.

I thought he was supposed to take over the financial side and let me get on with having children, becoming a house-wife like my mother. Of course this was not the man I married. I discovered, as time went on, he really was the complete opposite. I also discovered that if you don't communicate, you are doomed to failure.

It was once said that a relationship should be like the pillars of a temple both standing firm and independent. If they lean in or out too much, the temple will collapse. Both have to be solid and straight for the temple to remain strong. This was not the case with Andy and I. We were leaning in all kinds of directions. And worst of all, we didn't let each other know when we were tottering. The ectopics were the final straw for our relationship—our communication had broken down entirely by then. We were both hurting so much we did not know what to say and were fearful how to say it. We were certainly not supporting one another.

Please, dear reader, learn from my mistakes. Even when you are fearful of the answer, ask the question anyway. It's so much better to try to communicate because if you don't even try, you have failed just by not speaking.

Don't let your disasters get you down. Yes, you may find yourself grovelling on the floor, but each morning brings a bright new day—a fresh start to do things differently and get yourself back on your feet. I can tell you that because I was that person grovelling on the ground. It may not be the life you imagined you were going to have. I thought mine would be a housewife and mother, but the universe, God, higher power, whatever you like to call it, had other plans for me. I just had to discover them, and that's what you have to do if disasters hit your life too.

Decade Five from 40 to 50 years old

SIMPLIFY YOUR SKINCARE
AND YOUR LIFE

My fortieth birthday was the worst birthday I ever had. As all my friends know, I'm very big on birthdays. I like a big fuss made of them, so as I describe this to you you may be surprised because you would think I had a wonderful time.

My parents were going to the Caribbean for a holiday. They suggested I go with them to cheer me up and they would treat me for my birthday.

It sounds amazing when you tell people you spend your fortieth birthday in the Caribbean, staying with my uncle George, who lives on Tortola, one of the British Virgin Islands.

He was so kind to organise such an amazing day and a wonderful party for me. First he did a pig roast on the beach, and then everyone went back to George's house, which overlooks the harbour, for drinks and merriment till the late hours.

The truth is I never felt so alone in my whole life. There I was in a beautiful place surrounded by family and friends, but the trouble was they were George's friends. All I really wanted to do was forget about my birthday. Turning forty isn't good at the best of times, but when I had just separated from my husband and the chance of having children seemed to be slipping away, what was there to celebrate? And after all George's effort to make it such an amazing party, it just seemed to make my whole situation even worse. I felt even more of a failure, feeling guilty that I didn't want to be there and just so sad.

When Andy returned three months later, he told me he wanted a divorce. He was staying in Somerset with his father and was coming to London every so often, using our home as a hotel. I got fed up with this—he needed to go. So I changed the locks and put all his belongings into his car, which he wanted back. My little Mini had been stolen, so we only had the Golf. There was hardly room for him to get in; it was so full. He was furious at me and threw one of his bags of his things back at the front door, shouting abuse at me for all the neighbours to hear—not good for my reputation, especially as I had particularly odd neighbours at that time—but more on that later.

Now I had no job and no husband, so I was forced to go on the dole to be able to survive and keep our home. I planned on getting a lodger to help with the bills. The interest rate was over five percent on mortgages, but even with a lodger it was not going to cover everything with the sort of wage I could expect to get.

But staying on the dole was not an option for me morally. I remember Glynn, my brother in law, telling me that I'd be stupid to get a job when the government was paying the interest on my mortgage while the rate was so high, but this did not feel right to me. I could work—I just needed enough money to be able to pay for everything that we could afford when there were two wages coming in.

Luckily for me, the government had started a scheme to try to improve the economy. If you started a small business, they would pay you a monthly amount to support you for the first year. Also they taught various courses to give you information on developing a business plan and learning about keeping accounts.

This was just what I needed to get myself back on my feet. It was a bit risky—I had no clients to bring with me and had not been doing treatments for quite some time. Only when I was in the hospital with the second ectopic did I start again, doing treatments for other patients to cheer them up and give myself something to do to pass the time. I realised then how much I enjoyed doing treatments and had missed doing them when I was at Selfridges.

This was a risk worth taking, what did I have to lose? I was at rock bottom with my finances, none of the jobs I'd applied for had me very excited or paid enough to make it worth coming off the dole. This seemed like an opportunity to do something I'd only ever dreamed about. It was going to be hard work, but I never minded hard work when the outcome was something worthwhile.

So, Image Inspiration was born—this was the name I chose to cover all the hats I was wearing at that time. My main focus was to have my own beauty salon, but I didn't have any clients so that was the first hurdle to jump. To help make some money until I had enough clients to call what I was doing a beauty business, I joined a fashion company called Weekenders that sold clothing by doing parties in people's homes. Hence the name Image Inspiration—I felt it covered the two arms of my work quite nicely.

This was a great way to spread the word of what I did and also to get to meet new people at these events organised by my party host. All I had to do was convince people to hold a party. That wasn't difficult because once people enjoyed themselves, they were happy to host one, too, and get a discount on any clothes they bought.

It was so funny going to training courses with Weekenders because they had us set goals for expanding our business—I always substituted their fashion goals for my beauty business. That was expanding, too, until eventually I was able to stop doing parties because I had gained enough clients to call it a real beauty business.

It took three years till I felt brave enough to give up all my support. I also had two part-time jobs, one at a local restaurant, Christian's, waitressing on the evenings I wasn't doing parties, and the other was at London Lighthouse doing massage for people with HIV and AIDS. I'd started volunteering at their drop-in service doing manicures and pedicures. Then they offered me a paid position doing massage in the therapeutic department. This was the one I was most reluctant to quit. I enjoyed the work, as I could see how much good it did, but it was silly to remain there on a wage when I had my own clients who wanted my time.

So I was going it alone with one message and one vision— to build my own beauty business.

There were a couple of lucky things at the beginning that helped me on the way to making this a successful business once I streamlined my vision. Please take note, dear reader, that a well-focused vision backed up by action brings into play forces you never knew were available to you, which my second lucky break will show you.

When I first started on my own, I wanted to have Guinot as my skincare brand, but at that time there was a salon on Turnham Green Terrace in Chiswick that had sole rights to do the treatments and sell the products in the area. I have used many different skincare brands and products over the years Orlane, Ultima II and Revlon, Clarins, Sothy, Elmis to name a few you may be familiar with, also Arval, Dermalogica and Guinot. All these other brands were started by either a therapist or a business person. What impressed me about Guinot was that it was created by a pharmacist. Also, it was only sold by fully qualified therapists who would first diagnose by thoroughly looking at the skin before recommending a product. The range of products in the brand covered every sort of problem you may encounter on the skin.

It frustrated me not to be able to have my brand of choice, and for a while I felt like I was in no-man's land using Clarins creams and products from a beauty wholesaler. I realised I just had to commit to a product range. I was almost about to sign with Dermalogica when I heard through the grapevine that the other salon was being sold.

I immediately contacted Guinot to ask if I could now take on the brand, my first lucky break.

That was in 2000 and I have never looked back. It was a huge commitment at the time and very expensive to buy products and the equipment for the treatments, but I knew it was the right choice. These treatments and products had the most impact on my own skin and I believed in them.

The other lucky break for me was false tanning treatments. When I first came to London, you may remember I worked in a salon in Kensington, Violet Adairs. It was known as the go-to place for a believable false-tan, which back then was very hard to find. All the commercial ones on the market made you look a weird shade of orange and false tanning was not popular then at all. Violet Adair had their own product that was very good. All the actors and models came to us for a tan. They would come for a treatment before filming or a photo shoot and we'd apply it with Marigold washing up gloves because that's all there was back then to protect our hands from going brown. It was a clear cream which eventually turned your skin to a lovely tanned colour, but you had to be very good at applying it or there would be streaks—and that's the last thing you want on a close-up photo shoot.

So I became very good at doing the perfect tan. This was one of the treatments I offered in my business. I would use a range of different products—at first Clarins and Dermalogica, and eventually Guinot, doing a patch test first to see which colour was the best suited for my client.

This worked very well. In the meantime, I became a council member for BABTAC The British Association of Beauty Therapy and Cosmetology. This was the same year I took on the Guinot brand. While attending an industry exhibition on the stand for BABTAC, I learnt of St. Tropez—a new false tanning range that Judy Narke was introducing to the UK from the USA.

One of the girls on our stand looked very brown, and I asked where she got her tan. She said laughingly, "St. Tropez."

"When have you had time to go to St. Tropez?" I asked. She grabbed my arm and marched me over to the St. Tropez stand announcing that I must give it a try. I let them do my arms to try it out. It was amazing because it works with your own skin colour to produce the right depth of tan to suit you and was not at all orange.

I felt like a million dollars at the trade show party that night with my gorgeous tanned arms. The next day I bought everything I needed from St Tropez to add to my repertoire of tanning products for my clients. It eventually became obvious that this was a winner because when I did the patch test to check colour this was picked nearly every time, so I decided to concentrate on this product for tanning.

St. Tropez was becoming ever more popular with the press. I was the only person doing the treatment in West London, Judy was sending clients to me at an alarming rate, and I was working my socks off. But I'd never received official training to do the treatment. When an article came out in Vogue, the journalist going for the tan had the guide colour buffed off, I realised I was not doing this. My poor clients were going out looking like the bark of a tree. My clients trusted me when I said it would look perfect after they had showered off the guide colour, but they had to wait at least three hours before they were able to do this or it would stop the tan from developing. I called Judy to ask about training. She was really surprised I wanted to do this because everyone she sent to me was very happy. She'd never had anyone complain about me, but she booked me in. I really enjoyed the day, gaining loads of valuable lessons. My clients were so happy now that they could leave looking OK. One client told me she could now go put petrol in her car, which she wouldn't have dared do before.

This treatment, because of its popularity in the press and because my timing was perfect, boosted the number of clients coming to me, turning my fledgling business into something substantial and altogether worthwhile.

I was so busy, I started looking for somewhere larger to move the business so I could expand. I even got my NVQ assessor training certificate so I could take on apprentices.

It was at this time I met John.

I went to a talk by Jan Cicek about feng shui, the art of moving things in your home to create a positive effect in your life. I discovered all sorts of things, but the most useful at that time was how to discourage difficult neighbours. My flat was on the ground floor of a semi-detached house. My next door neighbours on the side I was attached to were an unusual couple with two children. The woman was friendly to start with, but after my husband left it became apparent she did not approve. I don't know if this was her Iranian background or because her husband was violent to her. At any opportunity, she called me names or accused me of doing awful things. It became so bad I dreaded walking out my own front door in case she was there.

On one occasion when I was parking my car, she accused me of hitting her car. Thank goodness my next client had come early. She was there to witness this accusation and told my neighbour that she had clearly seen me park perfectly and not touch anyone else's car.

On another occasion I heard shouting and banging in the house and went around to see if I could help. Her husband opened the door and, saying nothing to me, he turned to her saying, "Even the neighbours are coming around with your noise." He then closed the door in my face. So when an upstairs window broke with something hurtling out of it, I called the police. I knew the children were home and was afraid for their safety. I was also afraid of the repercussions, but the police told me I had absolutely done the right thing as most crimes come from domestic violence. But I still had to live next door to them.

At Jan's talk, he told us that if we were having problems with our neighbours, to put up a bagua mirror facing toward them so it would send all their negative energy back to them. I did what he said as soon as I got home and strangely, I felt much calmer as soon as it was in place. The amazing thing was that within a month they were gone. Apparently they went bankrupt and the house had been on the market for quite a while. I didn't know any of this till they left. Every time anyone showed any interest or came to view the house, they did all they could to stop the sale. How did the feng shui help? I have no idea. All I know is I was not troubled by these awful people ever again.

So what has all this got to do with John you might ask? Well, I lent my bagua mirror to two other people with similar problems and got two more success stories. I was so impressed I got back in touch with Jan Cisek to tell him, and he very kindly sent me another mirror with a fake diamond and a dime. He told me to put the dime into the money area of the bagua to strengthen that in my life. I should explain that a bagua mirror is octagonal and each area has a specific meaning in respect to different areas of your life. The diamond was to go in an area of my life that I wanted to strengthen. As my relationships were at an all time low that's where I put it. Presto! I met John a few weeks later.

EMOTIONS

Do you remember in the first decade I spoke about my mother not wanting to touch me as soon as I was born because she wanted me to be washed before she held me? Did that have an effect on me subconsciously? Maybe I had feelings of rejection then which were reinforced later.

My sister and I used to go to the nursing home my aunties ran. My mother helped out and my aunties loved to see us, so we were there most days. I was my auntie Nesta's favourite and she wanted me to come and sit with her all the time. My mother used to tell me to go and make sure that Auntie Nesta was okay. I know I was very resentful because I wanted to stay with my mother or play with my sister. I did not want to have to sit with my auntie everytime we went there. These emotions build up and begin to have an effect on our bodies if we don't release them in a controlled way. Emotions have a way of getting out of control, too, suddenly bubbling up to the surface when you least expect it.

I'm no expert on emotions, but I do know that if you don't do something to control your emotions they can end up controlling you. It's far better to learn what may trigger any negative emotion before it does your body serious damage. The damage that anger can do may start as little bursts of aggression on our face in the form of spots, according to Louise Hay in her book on how emotions affect our bodies.

Traditional Chinese medicine tells us that an imbalance of any organ first shows in a small way on the periphery of the body. Skin is usually an imbalance from the lungs and small intestine. The negative emotion associated with these organs is grief, and I certainly had been through plenty of grief trying to have children and then the break up of my marriage.

I believe these emotions made my skin worse. It was during that awful decade that my skin became red and inflamed with rosacea. I know there was a physical element that didn't help, but emotions upset the endocrine system, which in turn brings a response in the body—in my case rosacea, my weak area. Yours could be somewhere else in the body. There is usually a part that may have been weakened by genetics or lifestyle that is the area that, in your body's case, gets out of balance and sick when you are stressed or run down. People often think of stress being in our mind, but our environment, our diet, and lack of sleep all cause stress, too. We need to bear that in mind when our health begins to suffer.

Negative thoughts and emotions have a very detrimental effect on our health. They can spiral out of control. Do you remember I talked about stacking in Decade Two when I put off doing my accounts and the amount got so big I'd become overwhelmed? This can also happen with negative emotions—a negative thought leads to another then another until the initial problem has been blown out of proportion. You are reeling with total overwhelm with this massive stack of negativity. You must take control of what you put into your head. Become aware of the danger of letting negativity get out of control and stop it before it controls you.

I think resentment was one of the negative emotions that got way out of control in my life. It was probably a major factor in the breakdown of my first marriage. I thought I had good reason to be resentful. I probably did, but letting resentment take control does not make for a good life and certainly not a good marriage. I can see that it takes two to tango and I played my part in our separation and ultimate divorce. The important part is to learn and take responsibility for your own actions, not blame others and then be resentful letting that smoulder away damaging your health.

The first step is to be grateful for what you already have, the second step is to be aware of any negativity that comes up from that, and the third step is to stop yourself any time you start thinking in a negative manner. Stop going into that downward spiral and do something to change the pattern.

Skincare for forties

You may well have expanded on your anti-ageing regimen by now with eye creams and neck creams, but the basics must always remain. Cleaning in the evening and protection for the day.

This should be a healthy habit by now, just like brushing your teeth. If it's not, then what hope do you think any of those other products you may be tempted to get will stop the deterioration?

Just like the dentist tells you to keep brushing your teeth to keep them healthy, that's what I'm saying about cleaning and protection for your skin. It's essential to maintain skin health so that an anti-ageing regimen has a chance to do its job. I'm afraid that the older you get, the harder you have to work to keep yourself looking good in all areas of your life—health and fitness, too, not just the skin. The other steps we should be using now on this road to keep our skin looking good is a regular exfoliating regimen and the use of serums to add extra support.

So the next step on this quest to ageless skin is firming the skin's muscular support. This can be done with facial exercises, but like any type of exercise, it needs to be done on a regular basis, little and often, which is not always that easy to fit into our lives. To be honest, it would be better to have started earlier in life. Getting into a good habit when you thought you had no need for it. We never believe that our skins will eventually start to sag and bag as we get old. But unfortunately, around this time the jawline does not look so firm anymore and the nasolabial fold becomes just that—a fold. That's the line from your nose to the outer corner of your lips that has started to appear. Of course, everyone is different and ages in different ways, so you may have always had a line there or may never get one depending on how your genetic make-up and lifestyle have affected you. But however we look, the structure and support for our skin needs help at this age.

There are plenty of firming products out there on the market, but most are using retinol to make the skin feel firmer and have a tightening effect on the skin. Be careful how you use them because they can be firming at the expense of losing that youthful bloom by drying out the skin too much.

Remember to always monitor the effect of a product and change if necessary.

There are some marvellous treatments out there that can restore firmness if done on a regular basis, like using a micro-current either by going to a professional or getting a home kit to do on yourself. But like I was saying earlier about facial exercises, these must be done little and often to get good results.

Tools that can help our equilibrium

Let's look at some tools for staying centred and calm, like meditation and mindfulness, complementary therapies, Bach flower remedies and affirmations.

I mentioned earlier my interest in meditation—it has always fascinated me. But I'm also baffled that as humans we explore the far flung corners of the universe, but know very little about our own interiors. Yes, we understand the anatomy and chemistry of our bodies, but our spirit and soul—what do we know of these? I think meditation helps us explore this interior world and gets right down to the root of our being. It's not easy and requires discipline to make yourself invest the time to do it. It's very difficult and challenging to be silent and still, trying to ignore all the thoughts that keep popping up in your head. But that's the point of meditation slowing down the chatter in our heads and finding that peaceful place that will allow you to stay calm.

Once found, that calmness seems to stay with you as you work, dealing with other people and issues that come up through the day. It has definitely cured my headless-chicken mode which was my default way of operating before doing meditation. Yes, I still have moments when I revert to the old patterns, but I'm so aware when I do that I can pull myself out of it fairly quickly, and it's certainly less often these days, too.

I definitely recommend giving it a try if you are the sort of person who cannot concentrate on one thing at a time. Remember, being in the present moment is the only moment there is. The past is gone and there's nothing you can do about it. The future is still to come and has many options, but the present is the only time that can be affected by you. The past is history, the future a mystery, only the present is real. If you are not present in the present then you are wasting your life away. How sad is that?

Other tools that helped me are affirmations when things have not been going well and I needed a reminder to keep my head and mind focused and my life on track. I'm sure you have heard of mindfulness, which uses different ways to calm our thoughts. Affirmations, visualisation, and meditation exercises are used to do this. All are very useful, and each has its merits at certain times. I began using visualisation exercises originally to discover my interior world or subconscious. I then moved onto affirmations as a way to help guide my subconscious to a better place. But it was meditation that most helped me find a calmness that came from beyond me in a deeper part of my being. Some would call this faith, God's power, or universal energy, even describing it as intuition or spirit. Whatever you call it does not matter. What matters is finding this inner source of strength that can guide you and get you through the hard times—life's challenges that come to shape us and make us stronger.

There are complementary therapies that can help with mental health issues. One I have found very helpful for my clients and myself are the Bach flower remedies, which are a type of homoeopathic flower essence that you put on your tongue to absorb the active ingredient.

They are used to help balance out negative emotions. For example, I became very resentful of my ex-husband toward the end of our marriage. I discovered that when I used Willow from the Bach flower remedies, my resentment eased. As the negative emotions disappeared, I became more positive and focused on the good rather than the bad with any issue.

These are just some of the tools I have found useful over the years, but there are many more out there—different complementary therapies like massage, aromatherapy, daoyin tao and reiki to just mention the treatments that I do- you just have to find what works for you. Remember that if we are emotionally supported and calm, this will have a very beneficial effect on our skin and help keep the wrinkles away.

How do you survive?

So now you know some of the tricks I used to survive when life was handing me lemons. These tricks made me realise that lemons are great in gin and tonics, and you can make a mean lemon drizzle cake from them, too. In other words, you just have to see things in a more favourable light. As the song goes, "Always look on the bright side of life." Good old Monty Python.

I think it is really important we discover the things we love. I'm not talking about relationships here, although having someone to love and who loves you, too, is always good. Loving yourself and knowing what you enjoy, what makes you happy, is far more important. I actually think this is a prerequisite to having a healthy relationship with someone else anyway.

Too many people get stuck on the idea that someone else will make them happy, but actually it's the other way around. You need to know first what makes you happy before you can be happy with anyone else. A strong confident person who knows themselves, warts and all, is far more attractive than a pretty but needy person who is looking to the other to make them feel good.

So what do you enjoy? What makes you laugh out loud? What makes you get up that extra hour early in the morning to go do it?

I have a plaque on my wall in my dressing room that says, "Happiness is a journey not a destination." I love it. I remember finding that plaque and realising this was such a good reminder to keep on doing what you enjoy over and over again. When I say do what you enjoy, I don't mean all the big things, although I'd never turn down tickets to a Chelsea Flower Show or if someone offered me an amazing holiday. Of course those types of things make us happy, but you also have to find the small things, because not everyday is going to be a holiday. But you can make it as close as possible to that holiday feeling if you have some great things you love to improve on a bad day. For example, I used to treat myself to a cappuccino to cheer me up. Now I have invested in a coffee machine so I can have that experience at home any time and use it to start my day in a great way.

That is the trick—having as much around you as you can to make you smile.

It's the quality of our days that is important. If you go to sleep in a bad mood, you are more likely not to sleep well, then wake up grumpy. It does not bode well for the rest of the day. But if you go to sleep after remembering all the things you are grateful for, you will sleep better, and you are more likely to wake feeling good about the day ahead which improves the quality of the day. Give it a try. I recommend it.

Make sure that every day you have at least one small thing to look forward to—it may well be just wanting to get into your comfy bed, but be grateful that you have a comfy bed to get into. It's all about finding the good in any situation and making the most of that.

Decade Six from 50 to 60 years old

WE NEED TO GET SOME ORDER
AROUND HERE

Uh oh, here comes some more disasters. Most of us would say that life is a bit like a roller coaster—up and down. But this decade of my life was like riding the switchback at high speed.

I think no one would describe their lives as being flat and uneventful. We all have good and bad events throughout our lives, with hopefully nothing too major either way.

My skin was now reacting to all sorts of things and seemed to be permanently red with annoying little spots on my cheeks, chin, and nose. My treatment room was in my conservatory, and I hadn't realised how much sunlight I was getting on my skin—too much on a regular basis. Even though it was north facing, there was enough sunlight to be causing problems with my skin. I was not using the jane iredale™ foundation powder then. It has complete sun protection and that is what I needed.

My life with John started off fairly straight forward, but it was not going to be clear sailing.

When I first met John, he seemed too good to be true. He was such a gentleman, taking me to the best places, and we had such fun together.

We went to Paris for a weekend for his birthday. All the people from his studio came to see us off. Apparently he rarely took a holiday and was a bit of a workaholic, so this was a big event—actually taking time off—never mind being with me.

In Paris I had my first lesson about not going back to my old patterns when being in a relationship. We went on Eurostar when the London terminal was from Waterloo, so it was very convenient for us with a direct train from Chiswick. We got into Paris and decided to travel on the metro to our hotel rather than taking a taxi. Neither of us had any idea how the ticket system worked and were struggling with it when a chap came up to us and said he would help. I didn't have a good feeling about this, especially when he asked for a larger amount of money than I thought the ticket should be. He tried reassuring me, saying it was a multiple journey ticket and would last all weekend. I was just about to say, "No thank you," but John agreed and handed over the money. Of course this chap had seen us coming, speaking English and carrying our luggage. He must have thought, *Here is an easy way to make a buck.* We only had single tickets of course, which we realised when we got to the end of the journey.

I had been all around the world, to countless countries where we had been warned about this sort of thing happening, and never fell for it. But here I was playing the quiet little mouse again. I knew better, but did not speak up. This was not going to happen again. I learnt to trust my instincts, so why did I let John hand over the money? I did not want to show him up in front of this stranger, probably because we were still new in our relationship. But I also recognised this was an old pattern I'd learnt from my parents—the man knows better and should not be questioned when a decision is made. This did me no good in my marriage before, playing the quiet dutiful wife, so I'd better not stay quiet again.

It took a few more lessons to make this pattern stop altogether. Fortunately we didn't lose any more money, but it's still embarrassing to admit.

I was doing some personal development courses around the time I met John. One of them was held in Hawaii. We decided to have another holiday together in San Francisco. We made plans to meet there after I finished my course and then we'd fly home together. It was a great idea, but it never happened because while I was at training, two aeroplanes were driven into the Twin Towers in New York. September 11 is not a date many people will forget when the unthinkable became real.

What a shock to wake up to that news. Because of the time difference, I didn't hear about it straight away. I never saw any of the media footage until I got home. Maybe that was just as well as I may not have wanted to get on a plane to go home if I had. The majority of the people in the course were American, a lot from New York. It was awful for them not knowing if their loved ones had been caught up in it. Eventually we heard some truly harrowing stories from those who lost family and friends in the tragedy. We heard a phone call made by one of the participant's partner as he said good-bye to her from his office in the Twin Towers. It was truly the worst thing to hear and gives me the quivers just thinking about it as I'm writing this.

All air traffic was cancelled and I was stuck in Hawaii until it was reopened—what a hardship, but it's not quite the same all on your own. Even when I could leave, I could only get to San Francisco via Boston and then was stuck there for another week. John could not get to me or me to him—so much for our holiday. I ended up getting into another course to learn live blood analysis. It was very interesting and kept me occupied.

It was about this time that my sister noticed a large mole on my back. It was on the middle of my back around bra strap level. She told me I should get it checked by the doctor, but it took her telling me a few more times before I did. I couldn't see or feel it so, "out of sight, out of mind." Thank goodness for my sister because it turned out that it was a melanoma and luckily, it was caught early enough to be cut out safely without doing any more damage to my body.

I'm convinced the melanoma originated with a serious sunburn I got on my back in St. Thomas years ago when I worked on the ships, which was not helped by going on sunbeds once I returned home.

John and my relationship had an easy-going nature. We took turns going to each other's place for the weekend. But every now and then John went off-grid, not turning up and I could not reach him. His excuse when he eventually called was he'd been caught up with an urgent job at work. He'd be very sorry, sending me flowers or a gift to make up for it.

This pacified me to start with. I enjoyed the extra attention after the event, but he was becoming so unreliable. I was getting fed up, not knowing whether I was spending a weekend on my own or not. This was happening more often, so I decided to trust my instincts and find out what was happening. Keeping quiet was not on my agenda any more.

So on one of these occasions I drove over to his studio in Wandsworth. If he was there, no problem, I'd just say I came to surprise him. But when I got there, I found it was all shut up. He was not working, so what was he doing? I then decided to drive to his place in Catford. When I arrived, there was no reply at the door. I looked around the back to see if anyone was there. As I looked through the window, I discovered John completely out of it—a couple of empty bottles were on the floor and he was fast asleep on his sofa.

I drove home wondering what was I to do? I had not suspected this at all, but in retrospect it did not surprise me. He had a high-powered, demanding job and all the pressure that came with that. We needed to talk about it, not carry on as if it didn't happen. Clearly this had been happening on a fairly regular basis.

So life then took on a different picture. I was now going out with someone who thought he was just having a binge every now and then. He didn't realise it was a far worse problem than that.

I knew I had to look after myself and discover why I had been drawn to this kind of relationship.

Years ago I did a course with Dr. Christine Page, who has written many books on metaphysics, one of which is called The *Mirror of Existence*. I'd learnt that all relationships exist to help us to learn about different aspects of ourselves, so what was going on here? We were going through a very difficult patch, but often things have to reach rock bottom before they can come back up again.

I won a relaxing retreat weekend in Harrogate—lovely enough to go on a retreat but to win it?—so much the better. It's a funny thing about being lucky. It always seems to come along when I most need it. When I was on the dole and didn't have two pennies to rub together, I won £100.00 from the Premium Bonds. It was unbelievable because I didn't even know I had any Premium Bonds. It turned out I've only ever had one. You can't even buy one bond these days. Auntie Nesta got it for me when I was little, probably a birthday present when giving a child a pound was a lot of money. This bond was never a winner at any other time, not even for a small amount like £25.00 which my father seemed to win on a regular basis, but just when I needed it the most—there it was. I really needed this weekend away, too—having someone else look after me for a change and having nothing to do or think about but enjoying myself.

I took the train there. It was weird going through Doncaster station and not stopping off to see my family, but this weekend was for me and me alone.

Anna Louise Haigh has the most beautiful, spiritual practice in her lovely welcoming home. She made me feel very special and pampered. I enjoyed amazing treatments, lovely food, and just being looked after. At the end of the weekend she told me she would do a soul reading for me. I had to pick whichever of the lovely stones and crystals I was drawn to. She would then tell me what it all meant. She told me I already overcame difficult times, but things were getting better. Eventually I would have all that I wanted, but before that happened I had to go through one more very difficult challenge.

I didn't like the sound of this at all. Surely I had been through enough dealing with two ectopic pregnancies, a divorce, my brother's death and the scare of skin cancer—but whatever it was I knew I would just have to cope.

Soon after I returned home I was awakened one night by a phone call.

I'd already had a few trips to the hospital with John when he'd overdone it so much with the binge drinking he'd had to call an ambulance. This phone call was different. I rarely have my mobile phone in the bedroom, preferring to keep my bedroom calm and serene. Luckily, it was by my bed and it woke me with a jolt. I could barely make out what John was saying, but knew instinctively that I had to get there as fast as I could. John had now reached rock bottom—he saw nowhere else to go. Was his call a cry for help or just to say goodbye?

When I arrived at John's, I went on autopilot, calling 999 and explaining the situation. The person on the other end of the line was brilliant and told me exactly what to do. Soon help arrived in the form of a paramedic and then the ambulance. I could do no more—his life was in the balance and I just had to pray.

Anna Louise was right. This was something I never ever want to have to go through again. It was a very difficult challenge indeed. We were lucky though. We both came through it with just a few scars. "Things can only get better," as they say, and luckily for us they did.

I'm very proud of John. It was not easy, but after recovering from this he has turned his life around.

GENES AND ETHNICITY

What we are born with—inherited from our parents—is going to play a part in how well we age. Some of us will be lucky and have good genes, others will not. I discovered I inherited a skin that was more prone to rosacea from my father, but it was a long time after dealing with the condition that I realised this.

Rosacea comes in different stages which progress as the condition becomes more severe if not treated. Type one vascular rosacea starts with a mild blushing of the skin which becomes worse when the person is exposed to certain conditions that can trigger the redness. This can progress to a more constant redness with small blood capillaries becoming visible. Type two is inflammatory rosacea—the inflammation is caused by the constant irritation from the overactive capillary, redness and red bumps (papules) and pus-filled spots (pustules) appear on the skin. Type three phymatous rosacea comes from this continued irritation and inflammation causing the epidermis to thicken and maybe become bumpy, especially on the nose. The persistent facial redness looks like a constant blush or sunburn that does not go away. Type four ocular rosacea is not so common, but can be the first sign to developing facial rosacea. It is an inflammation that causes redness, itching and burning around the eyes. All types are made worse from certain triggers.

It is a good idea to discover what your triggers are—in my case, certain spicy foods and red wine—but this is not the same for everyone. There are external triggers, too—for me the sun and going from different extremes of temperature, like coming into a central heated house from being outside in the cold.

It was more common to get rosacea as one aged, but because of the way we look after our skin—using more and different kinds of products—I'm seeing this condition in more and more young people.

When I did my training it was called acne rosacea, probably because of that inflammatory stage. Unfortunately it was treated more like an acne condition which made it worse. So little was known about it then. I have spent my whole career getting to understand it and finding the best ways to treat it. I get so cross when I still hear it described as acne rosacea and hear it being treated in that way. Therapists, doctors and dermatologists should know better now.

It needs to be treated with a great deal of sensitivity and care. This is a complex condition with many factors that can trigger it.

One thing that has a huge impact and is not really given enough attention is our ethnicity because even though little research has been done on the effects of ethnicity on the skin, it plays a part that cannot be ignored.

The major groups where research has been conducted are African, Asian, and Caucasian. Because my clients are mostly Caucasian, I took it a step further, describing Caucasian skin types as either Celtic or Mediterranean because I can see that the stratum corneum was thinner, lighter, and more delicate on the Celtic Caucasian skin and was thicker, darker, and more robust on the latter. This also ties in nicely with the Fitzpatrick scale.

I think you can probably break down African and Asian, too, from their different regions. With the melting pot of ethnic mix you find here in London, perhaps asking someone what they consider their ethnicity to be is an easier way of finding out, than asking them where they are from.

The obvious difference with African skin is the amount of pigmentation, which of course gives them a massive advantage when it comes to anti-ageing because their skin is so well protected from the sun—which we know has the most impact when it comes to premature ageing. But this can also be a disadvantage for them. Because of the extra amount of melanin in their skin, they are more prone to pigmentation trauma—keloid scarring plus pigmentation marks are more common as they age. What may not be known is that this ethnic skin type does not produce as much ceramides as the other groups so it can be drier and does not desquamate— shed skin cells—as easily. This also may be one reason why ageing African skin can look ashen.

An Asian ethnic skin type has a thinner stratum corneum and a higher eccrine gland density which appears to make their skin more sensitive. But they have a higher water content and higher lipid levels which reduces TEWL (transepidermal water loss) and makes their skin slower in ageing. Even though they have less pigmentation than an African skin, it appears these other factors also slow ageing. This is good news for us all because we can all help our lipid levels and water content with good lifestyle choices and proper skin care.

Skincare for fifties

Cleanse in the evening, protect during the day—what a great mantra this makes. I hope it is still a regular part of your skincare regimen. I know how easily the basics can be lost when we are trying to do all these treatments and use other creams to make ourselves look good.

At this time in our lives we have the effects of menopause. You may be going through this transition naturally or through help with hormone replacement therapy (HRT), but there are challenges with our skin either way. The hormonal disruption affects the skin in a similar way to our teens and twenties, but not usually as bad regarding spots and acne. This may be the case with you. Remember we all have different reactions when it comes to hormones, but eventually, whichever route you have taken, a lack of oestrogen in our bodies from the menopause will make the skin dryer and lose its youthful bloom and fullness. And another thing you may be noticing now are the effects of glycation, read on for further information about this.

Makeup can be your best friend or your worst enemy.

"The most beautiful makeup for a woman is passion.
But cosmetics are easier to buy."
-Yves Saint Laurent

Love it or hate it, makeup can be your best friend or your worst enemy. I didn't really grasp makeup till I was at sixth form college. I copied the makeup technique I saw on a picture of an Estee Lauder model, and that made a big difference in both my confidence and my appearance—so much so that when I didn't have any makeup on people asked if I was not feeling well. This came in very handy. If I wanted to go home early from work, I just put less makeup on and that did the trick.

Previously I'd tried a little lipstick or mascara, but never really knew what to do. After my training, I realised there was an art to application that needed to be learnt and practised regularly after finding the look that makes you happiest.

I'm not going into a whole rigmarole on makeup application here—I think that could be another book in itself. Suffice it to say that taking the time to master makeup can be a life saver, especially on bad hair days when you just need something to boost your confidence when everything else around you is going wrong.

Consider going for a makeup lesson to master makeup technique if you don't feel confident doing it yourself. Take a picture of someone you think looks good and similar to you, as I did with the Estee Lauder model.

You can pay for makeup lessons with someone you feel happy and confident with or has been recommended to you. The one-on-one personal attention and advice can be invaluable if you have no idea what to do.

I also suggest going to the makeup counters in large department stores because this is what they are trained to do. It is free, but they expect you to buy the makeup they have used. If you don't mind other people watching as you get your makeup done, this can be a cheaper way to try a new look. You don't have to buy any of the cosmetics from them, just say after they have finished that you would like to see the makeup in daylight and live with it before you purchase anything and could they please write down what they have used.

You should always check your new look in the daylight, whichever route you choose, before purchasing any products because makeup does look different in artificial light. What looked fine indoors can be too strong and garish in the sunlight.

I'd like to tell you why I said that makeup could be your best friend or your worst enemy. On a physical level, it enhances your appearance and makes the most of your best features when applied well. On an emotional level, it is brilliant for your confidence and can boost self-esteem, especially when you get compliments on how good you look. It also can be very self-nurturing spending ten minutes applying your makeup, putting your best face forward each morning. When you feel you look good it makes you feel better, when you feel better you have more energy and can accomplish more. You become more outgoing and friendly to other people and that passes on to them. It's a great thing all around.

One of my favourite little ditties is, "If I smile at you it makes you smile, too. This smile becomes infectious and spreads happiness as it goes. Let's keep smiling at each other and conquer all our foes."

This is the powerful and friendly face of makeup, but it has a dark side too, becoming your worst enemy. On a physical level, makeup applied badly can look awful and if it's not removed correctly, can ruin your skin. Remember the client I had in Oxford who never used a cleanser at all. Emotionally you need to be careful you do not use it as an armour, which then can easily become a crutch.

I got so hooked on my makeup I would not be seen without it. At first I would not go out of the house without it, then it got so bad I would not open the door if someone came around. I was so afraid of what people would think of me looking so awful without my makeup. It didn't help that my skin was going through an awful bout of rosacea because of the disasters in my life. Because I was in the beauty profession I thought I always had to look good, but all this did was erode my confidence and self-esteem. It became a sophisticated mask for me to hide behind. If you recognise this in your own behaviour then please take steps to correct it.

My first step was to correct the skin problem so I was not just hiding the mess of my skin. As it improved, I didn't need as much makeup to feel safe. Then I began to use less on days I was not working till eventually I could go without. With any addiction, it needs to be tackled at a pace you feel happy with. I was addicted to makeup at that time and I still feel the need to apologise to people who see me without makeup for the first time. My skin is so pale they often think I am sick—in COVID times, that was not a good thing.

How do you cope?

We all cope differently and there is no wrong or right way. It's finding what works for you. I need to talk and get it out there. Sharing what's wrong with another person helps to lighten the load and sometimes they may come up with solutions you hadn't thought of or help you see things differently or from another perspective which can help, too.

So how do you cope? It is good to recognise what works for us, and then remember to use it when it's needed. Often when we are hurting, we forget that we can help ourselves with these coping strategies. We are so lost in the hurt, we forget to use them.

And as I have said before, these challenges are making us stronger. Each time we overcome a small difficulty or a large disaster, we learn more about ourselves and find different ways to cope. The more tools we have in our personal tool box the easier we can then cope with the next challenge or disaster. Eventually we seem to be sailing along blissfully unaware of the storms that come and go. Believe me, you will always have something to deal with. It is so much better to realise that and just move forward, knowing you have come out the other side before and can do it again. Don't dwell on the problem. It's much better to look for the solution and take action to start moving out of the pain.

We also need to grieve if there is loss involved. I didn't really grieve the loss of my three babies. I was so young myself when I had the abortion and just wanted to not even think about what had happened—I was so ashamed. The two ectopic pregnancies were so painful and emotional that I just buried all those feelings, because I just had to keep on surviving with what was happening in our marriage. It was the first COVID lockdown that gave me the opportunity to go over this time in my life and finally grieve and accept the pain I had experienced. A book by Jodie Day *Living the Life Unexpected* made me realise I had not grieved their loss. I know the damage that can be caused by unexpressed emotions in our bodies if they are not released. I believe my cancer scare was one such nudge to look after myself and give myself time to go within to deal with the pain.

Do you have an incident or painful experience that has been buried and may now be causing you discomfort in your body? Buried emotions can cause disease and trauma in the body. We are meant to deal with these emotions and learn the lessons that can make us stronger and better able to cope with life.

Decade Seven from 60 to 70 years old

LEARNING HAPPINESS AND
HARMONY IN OUR SKIN

So this is where I am in my life right now—"rising seventy" as my father would love to point out. After passing a big birthday, in my case 66, you suddenly were rising to the next big number. It was not so bad when I was only in my teens and wanted to be older but is not so great for me now. Who wants to be told they are nearly five years older than they really are?

My skin has begun to sag and bag a bit now that I am this age. Unfortunately for me, I didn't have the benefit of this advice when I needed it. I don't have rosacea flare-ups except when I have a glass of wine—which I do like now and then—but it does not cause any irritation and recedes quickly. I was always lucky enough not to look my age, but I think I do now that I am over sixty. Despite all I have done since, the damage was done years ago, and at sixty it started to show. That's not bad, as I have seen it show on others at a much younger age.

They say life begins at fifty, but I'd say for me it really was sixty. In 2016, John and I got married. It was a very special day with all our family and friends around us in our local church. The only sadness was losing my mother. We had her funeral the week before our wedding. I know my poor father found it very difficult.

Getting married at an elderly age runs in the family. My auntie Kathleen, who I'm named after, was married for the first time when she was in her sixties. Unfortunately, she wasn't married very long when her husband died. I hope I'm a bit luckier.

We got married on the 29th of February, a leap year, which means we only have an anniversary every four years. I thought this would make it easier for John to remember. We didn't plan a honeymoon because of the situation with my mother's health and ended up having a mini-moon. My lovely sister-in-law Nikki came up with the idea of treating us to a stay at Cliveden for our wedding present. It was very luxurious and I was looking forward to having some great spa treatments there. Unfortunately, they were doing renovations in the spa, so the treatments were not quite as luxurious as they would have been normally. We eventually had our honeymoon on our first anniversary—four years later on the next leap year, 2020.

When I was on the ships, the only place I didn't see was South Africa, so my lovely husband took me there for our honeymoon. It was wonderful. We spent the first few days in Cape Town and met up with one of John's old business partners who was living there. Then we hired a car, did the garden route stopping at some beautiful places in the wine area and on the coast, until we finally came to Port Elizabeth. From there we drove up into the mountains to go on a safari in Adu Elephant Park. We had a lovely cabin that looked out over the spectacular scenery—vast areas of wilderness and a water hole where the animals came to drink.

It was while we were on a trip to see giraffes, elephants, and lions that we met a lady from the north of England who was just starting her holiday. She told us about the buying panic back home—there was real difficulty getting loo rolls. I hardly believed her and thought maybe it was just up north, because when we left there was no problem at all.

Little did we know, we would come back to a very different world than we had set out from.

This was the beginning of a world pandemic, COVID-19 had spread onto every continent. It was killing people and no one knew how to stop it. So the world went into lockdown to try to prevent the spread. Each country had to do something to stop being overwhelmed with the amount of people that needed hospitalisation to be put on ventilators to keep them alive.

It was disastrous for all those who lost loved ones. It was horrendous for the economy and so many individuals who now had no work—including me. It hit the professional beauty industry very badly. We were not allowed to work for nearly six months. When we did get back to doing treatments, it was very different with all the new protocols in place to keep everyone safe.

This was the end of my normal working life as I'd known it for nearly the past fifty decades. Yes, the beauty industry has changed beyond recognition from when I first qualified in 1974, but that was a gradual rearranging which gave you time to adapt. Now, after COVID, we were doing one thing one minute and then learning to do it completely differently the next. All protocols had to be evaluated to see if they were safe and would not put ourselves or our clients in danger. Some treatments were not viable anymore with the new protocols in place.

Even though the situation was very bad for a lot of people, including me, it became an opportunity. I was finding out what it would be like to retire without actually retiring. I had time to reevaluate my life and what was important to me—but all this took a while to realise. At first it was just the shock of being shut down. We were all so very lucky that the weather was kind to us here in the UK during the first wave of lockdown. At first I just felt like I was continuing my holiday. It was so lovely to be able to enjoy all the work that had been done on the house. This was the first opportunity I had to sit on my new patio in the sunshine, so I made the most of it. Then I began researching and taking certificates in COVID safety protocols so that when we reopened I was ready. Remember to always be prepared for all opportunities as I have said before.

AGEING

Most women at sixty have probably gone through menopause, but like me, you may still feel some of the symptoms. I always think this is a good thing, because it means there are some hormones working somewhere. I'm not sure if that is true or not, but it does make me feel better to think about it.

We start to age as soon as we are out of puberty—usually between sixteen to twenty five years old, as everyone ages differently. Up until puberty our bodies are constantly growing, after puberty they go into decline. We don't notice this too much, as it happens gradually, but after the stop of hormonal production from menopause, it is quicker and far more noticeable.

Menopause is officially the day twelve months after the last day of the last time you had a period. The time preceding this day is called perimenopause, and after that official day you are then postmenopausal. There are many symptoms related to menopause, the most common being hot flushes, night sweats, and mood swings.

Unfortunately, as far as our skin is concerned, menopause is not a good thing because of the changes in our hormone levels. The effects of the reduced oestrogen and progesterone hormones during perimenopause cause numerous physical symptoms on our bodies, including the skin, and these symptoms can carry on well after that single day one year after your last period.

Oestrogen especially affects the skin, as we need it to help maintain collagen and elastin—the building blocks that create skin structure and keep our skin firm and supple. As the levels diminish, our skin does not produce as much collagen and elastin. It is more prone to wrinkle and sag. Of course, gravity is also affecting everything going south, too, so it's not just due to lower hormonal levels.

Not everyone suffers during this time. We all age differently. Diet and lifestyle definitely make a difference, although very little research has been done in this area. Indigenous women in Japan don't even have a word for menopause in their language because they don't get the symptoms we do in the west. This is thought to be because of their diet and lifestyle.

You may notice that your skin does not bounce back as quickly as it used to. We would do a pinch test on the back of our hands to see how quickly or not the skin would regain its shape. One of the things you may notice when you get to this age is waking up in the morning with a pillow mark on your face that seems to take forever to disappear.

I did a little survey with my clients to see who slept on their backs, side, or tummy—which is what I do. It occurred to me that if we slept on our backs, gravity would give us a face lift as we slept. Those that slept on their backs definitely had smoother skin, gravity helping to keep the skin in place and stopping everything falling forward. But it is so hard to break a habit of a lifetime. As much as I tried, I always slept better on my tummy.

Skincare for sixties

Some of you reading this book who are at this age and have been doing the complete opposite of what I have been saying to keep your skin looking good may be wondering if there is any hope. It depends on how bad the skin is. Unfortunately, now is the time we can see the damage that has been done earlier on our skin. I know I have not always practised what I preach, and it's because of this that I know the pitfalls and what can be done or avoided at an earlier age to prevent them. The things I know now that are preventable—or at least may not be as bad if you follow my recommendations—are pigmentation marks, clogged capillaries (often called broken, but clogged is a more accurate way of describing them—the official name is telangiectasies), and horrid crusty growths that do not disappear no matter how often I exfoliate. These are senile warts, seborrheic keratosis, or lesions. (Why do we always have so many names for these things?) Whatever they are called, it is better to get them checked professionally to make sure there is nothing more sinister happening as these could be a melanoma or another skin cancer which can be prevented if it's checked out early enough.

My motto: If in doubt, check it out.

Once you know what you are dealing with, you can find the appropriate treatment. There is hope to lessen these skin problems, but prevention is better than cure. If you are a younger reader, please bear that in mind. It takes time and money to correct the damage—far better not to get that bad in the first place. That's why I'm writing this book, so you know with the information we have today how you can make the best of your skin. It's true that as time goes by, we discover better ways to keep ourselves looking good. But don't rely on that happening. Take care right from the start—it's definitely worth it.

So carry on with the basic cleansing and protection, exfoliate regularly, use serums for deeper anti-ageing skincare, and professional anti-ageing facial treatments if you have the time and can afford it for that extra boost.

I am often asked, "How often should you do a professional facial treatment?" The answer is the same whatever your age—once a month if you can afford it. Why? Because your skin replaces itself every fourteen to thirty days, depending on your age—the older you are, the slower this is. Treating these new skin cells each month keeps them looking good. But if you can't manage monthly treatments, then try and do a facial on the change of season—every three months. Because these seasonal weather changes put more pressure on the skin, a facial is a good way of combating that. And if you can't manage quarterly, then try to have a facial once a year just to make sure you are properly looking after your skin yourself.

You can of course come for a facial every week, but not many people have the time and money for that. Weekly home care on top of your daily routine will fill this gap. This is something I suggest even to clients who come regularly for monthly facials. The more care we give ourselves the better we will be.

Beware of marketing hype

Is there a perfect product? Let me tell you about a product called Creme de la Mer, first produced in the 1950s. It was first marketed as the only cream you would ever need to use—no need for day, night, eye, or neck creams, and that's why it was so expensive. It was the first cream to cost over £100! This was a huge amount to spend on face cream. You have to remember, we were only just out of the age when Pond's Cold Cream was all that was available.

Estee Lauder took over its production in 1996. I see now on the Creme de la Mer counter there are loads of different creams. What happened to it being the only cream you'd ever have to use?! Beware of marketing hype. There is no such thing as the perfect cream that will suit all.

Back in the fifties there really was only one cream, Pond's Cold Cream, that had to do every job for your skin. It was a cleanser and a moisturiser, eye makeup remover, and neck cream. It was only when Helena Rubinstein and Elizabeth Arden came onto the scene that this all changed. They were in a competitive war to sell the most products, so we suddenly had cleansers, toners, moisturising creams for daytime, nighttime, dry skin, oily skin, and the list goes on and on. It's completely out of hand now. I'm not saying we only need one cream—the example of Creme de la Mer shows that. But it's more important to pick the correct cream for the job it needs to do on your skin and the environment in which you live.

I discovered how important my environment was when I went to Tortola in the Caribbean. I did not get my suitcase from the airline between Antigua and Tortola. The airline company is called LIAT, jokingly referred to as "Leave island any time" or "luggage in another terminal."

So I ended up with no creams because they were all in my suitcase. Now I don't go anywhere without some cream in my hand luggage. Someone very kindly lent me some clothes, and she put in a couple of creams. I didn't really look very carefully at the cream before putting it on my face. It started burning my skin. It was a hair removal cream! Luckily I washed it off straight away and it didn't do too much damage. The other cream wasn't much better, so I ended up not using anything and was worried how my skin would be after the shock of the hair removal cream on my skin. Fortunately, my skin was fine. This was mostly because the atmosphere in the Caribbean is very humid and a humid atmosphere does not dry out the skin. Your natural protective mantle is replaced quickly when removed and doesn't have to work as hard because there's reduced TEWL (transepidermal water loss), so your skin will stay plumped up and hydrated even without a cream.

This taught me a very good lesson, even though I knew that it was important to match the correct type of moisturiser to skin type. For example, dehydrated skin needs oil in water lotion and dry skin needs water in oil cream. It hadn't occurred to me till that time that the outside atmosphere was just as important to take in consideration when picking a cream for your skin.

When you are taking a trip abroad, consider the climate to which you are going and then decide what type of cream is most appropriate for your skin and the climate.

What do you desire?

I always thought it would be lovely to be recognised, to do something that the world makes a big fuss about and shows its appreciation. But fame and fortune, I now see, is not all that it is cracked up to be. Being famous can mean losing your private life to the newspapers and media. There are pros and cons to everything.

I realised that my job was doing good, if only on a small scale. People felt better when they came for treatment. After a treatment, they would be nicer to the people with whom they came into contact. It would then radiate out from there. So even though my contribution seemed small to me, it was having a larger effect as it went out into the world.

I think the pandemic made people realise that we all contribute to the wider community however big or small our job may be. This contribution will be for the good of all, especially if we feel good inside and pass this on to others.

We have certainly realised that what may be considered a not very important job before, like a delivery driver or cleaner, is now seen as one of the most important jobs of all. God has always needed footsoldiers and considered them most important, even if we haven't. Captain Tom proved this when he raised money for the NHS from just walking around his garden. It was not what he did, but the attitude with which he did it. I loved his saying, "Today is going to be a good day." I think this positive attitude is what is most important with whatever we do.

What is it that you love to do? Can you make a living from it? If not a living, can it be a hobby that keeps you uplifted and inspired as you go about your working day? Not all of us can do what we love, but all of us can love what we do. However menial it may seem to you, is it bringing a benefit to all? Maybe in an indirect way, similar to my job, yours radiates from those you come into contact with to person after person.

Sometimes we have to do a job we are not thrilled with that helps us move toward something we would rather be doing, as I did when I sold clothes for Weekenders. The important thing is to always have your end goal in mind and keep moving toward it, trusting that the universe is supporting you if it is for the highest good of all.

Decade Eight from 70 to 80 years old

IT'S NOW THAT WE BECOME TRULY BEAUTIFUL

I'm not at this age yet, as you discovered in the previous decade. Because I'm still in my sixties, I obviously haven't had the experience of this age, so I thought I would use my mother's experience as an example of what happens at this time of life.

My mother was a wonderful lady, very kind and caring, and a brilliant cook. My mother and father did loads of entertaining. It was their greatest pleasure. When we were old enough, we used to do the washing up at large dinner parties to make a bit of extra pocket money.

My mother had wonderful skin and never looked her age. Hopefully I'm blessed with that, too. I know I have the same lines around my mouth as she did. That was not something I particularly wanted to inherit, but the good news is that all my life people have said I look just like her, so there is hope that I age as well.

My mother was severely dyslexic and apparently one of her teachers told her she better find a good man because she wasn't up to anything else academically.

From school she went to work at a hairdressing salon, but she ended up coming over to England to help out my aunties at the nursing home. That's where she met my father, and the rest is history, as they say. She definitely found her good man!

She was very particular about her appearance. She had her hair done on a regular basis and wore makeup up every day, so it was normal for my sister and I to see someone care for their skin and apply makeup. That became normal for us, too.

Only when I went away to boarding school did I realise that my mother was the exception, not the rule. The other girls' mothers were not as glamorous, nor were any of our teachers. Only Miss Harris, the choir mistress, was anywhere near as well dressed as my mother.

The other girls thought my mother was French. My sister and I used to laugh because we knew she was not that exotic—it was partly her fading Irish accent, but mostly her good looks.

One of the problems when I first went to boarding school was that I was not able to do my own hair because my mother always did it for me. After the first term, unfortunately, I had to have my hair cut short so I could cope with it. If you look at the picture of me in Decade Two, you will see my lovely, long plaits done by my mother every day.

It was also my mother's idea for me to do beauty therapy training, so I have a lot to thank her for. As my mother was entering her seventies, she was suffering from dementia. We first realised this when she started using salt instead of sugar in the meals she was cooking—quite revolting when you are expecting a lovely sweet dessert. She'd always been a bit forgetful and because of her dyslexia, she got things mixed up or the wrong way around. In fact, my father had a great time using her mistakes as the butt of his jokes. One of our favourites was, "You're a right pair, you three." She never got to live that one down.

Sue and I definitely knew there was something wrong when she came down one morning with blusher all over her face like a red Indian. It was time to hide all her makeup because you never knew how it was going to end up on her face. At this age she still had very good skin. I think it was from her good skincare routines, but mostly because she never put her face in the sun if she could help it. I never saw her sunbathing. She sat in the shade reading a book if she had to be outside at all.

This meant she had hardly any of the usual pigmented lesions you see on people of her age. She had just a few from gardening, but they were easily hidden with makeup. When my sister did her makeup for a special occasion she looked amazing and certainly not her age. It also helped that her red hair had only faded slightly as she aged and not gone grey.

It was such a pity that dementia took away her ability to speak. I knew it was very frustrating for her as it was leaving. This frustration showed in her expressions which on some occasions were not very attractive to see and made her look very old.

So remember a calm mind makes for a more serene and beautiful skin. If you are tense, uptight, angry, or frustrated as Mum was at times, it will show on your face. First, it appears as just an expression, but if this negative mood remains and becomes habitual, you will end up with permanent expression lines. Far better to have lines from smiling rather than from frowning.

Luckily, it was only at the end of my mother's life that she got bad tempered from vascular dementia. So even though at those times she looked, in her words, like an old hag, overall, when she was happy she looked very good for her age.

DIET AND LIFESTYLE

I have been talking a lot about diet and lifestyle throughout this book, but there is a good reason for this. Science now knows that the way we live our lives contributes far more to how healthily we age than the genes which we inherited. What we inherit must always be taken into consideration and we should make sure we mitigate any known health issues our parents and extended family have had, but how we live our lives may or may not do more damage. The choice is yours.

There is a body process which if it gets out of balance can have a detrimental effect on your health. I have known about this for a while and I'm still surprised that doctors don't check it on a regular basis with blood pressure, cholesterol and insulin levels.

The process in the body is called methylation and it happens in all our cells, but if this process does not have certain nutrients it can go astray and cause a chemical called homocysteine to rise. When tested, it is a good guide that our bodies may be out of balance. It's very easy to correct with the right supplements of B6, B12, folate, and omega-3. This will then bring the level of homocysteine back down again.

The reason you don't want to have elevated homocysteine is because this can be a precursor to other problems in the body such as heart disease, diabetes, and stroke. But most interesting for me is its positive effect on dementia, which comes from 1 percent of our genes—good news for me! The rest is diet and lifestyle.

I have gone on repeatedly, I know, about how diet and lifestyle affect the skin. I'm sure you all get it now. But the skin is only a gateway into the larger picture of what is going on in your body. If you want to live healthy to over ninety with all your wits about you, able to get around easily without help from walking sticks or zimmer frames, and not having to pop pills to make you feel OK, then you really need to make adjustments to your diet and lifestyle now if you think you are in any danger of succumbing to the above.

The doctors are always amazed that I'm not on any kind of medication. Apparently when you are over fifty, you will probably be on statins for cholesterol, insulin for Type 2 diabetes, or Warfarin for blood thinning. Apparently, I should be rattling from all these drugs at my age. Every one of these conditions are preventable by having a good diet and lifestyle. Yes, of course, some people are more susceptible to a condition if it runs in the family, but that's even more reason, in my opinion, to do as much as possible to mitigate the genes with an even better diet and lifestyle.

Doing this does not mean you can't enjoy yourself. It's just being sensible that when you go a bit overboard with too much alcohol or excess sugar or fat in your diet, you take it easy for a while to correct the damage. The body is wonderful. It will always try to get back into balance, and given the correct conditions, it usually does.

As I have said before, disease is the body's way of asking us to autocorrect something that is not really suiting us for our higher purpose—so always pay attention to its signals and messages.

Another reason we should avoid all those sugary foods, apart from the waist line, is that they cause a process in our skin and bodies called glycation. This is when proteins are affected by high glucose levels and cause the protein to harden. It appears as a type of quilting on the skin, usually beginning around the eyes. It looks like the little cushioning bits on a quilt. These can extend elsewhere on the face, especially the cheeks.

High levels of glucose in our bodies from diet will of course cause type 2 diabetes which has serious implications for your health, so our skin appearance is not the only reason we should monitor our diet.

Skincare for seventies

I have plenty of beautiful clients coming to me in their seventies and eighties. Some have done better than others at looking after their skin over the years, but all say that after their facial treatment their skin looks and feels better. How long that feeling and look lasts after the facial depends on how they have looked after their skin before and how they continue to look after it. Like most things in life, the more effort you put into it the better the results.

I may be tempted to go down the Botox and filler route by the time I get to seventy, and that's not so long now, but I think it's unlikely. It's funny, the older I get the less important how I look becomes—like sitting in front of this computer with no one looking at me. Perhaps I do think differently when it's a Zoom call and I can see all the sags and bags highlighted on the screen. Age brings a certain self-confidence. It can also make you invisible unless you stick up for yourself.

Our skincare is the same as before with the basics. The more extras you can do, like facials, will help. Although we may be tempted to add more makeup to cover the areas we are not so happy with, beware of overdoing it. Also beware of thinking that it's not worth the effort. It's amazing what a bit of makeup can do to enhance eyes, lips, and skin tones. It really made a difference in the way my mother looked toward the end of her life.

She used to say, "Please make sure I have my makeup on when I die, because I look half dead without it."

I'd reply, "But Mum, you will be whole dead." My sister was the brave one who did Mum's makeup for her funeral and she did a lovely job. I'm sure Mum was very pleased.

You can do anything if you put your mind to it

It's only concentrated thought patterns with a firm intention, followed by action that eventually brings something into being. That was proved with quantum physics, although I've probably simplified it a bit.

An example of this in my life is when I eventually managed to buy the upstairs flat, getting the whole house. I started off just thinking it was a good idea. I had no idea how I was going to manage it. I had no money and it wasn't for sale, but I really liked this idea. It occurred to me that this was probably the only way I was going to get a whole house with the price of property in Chiswick. I got an idea from going to a talk on feng shui by Jan Cisek. When I asked him what I needed to do with feng shui to help buy the flat above, he said if I grew some climbing plants from my flat up to the second floor flat, it would eventually encourage the flat to be mine. I had Russian vine and ivy growing up the walls to the point that it was going into the gutters, lifting the roof tiles, and endangering the whole house. So I got back in touch with Jan to tell him that this was really not a good idea, and asked what else I could do. This time he said to take a photo of myself in front of the whole house and put it in a prominent place.

I took a photo in autumn before the leaves dropped off the Russian vine looking beautiful and red behind me, and before the following spring, with the vine still leafless I was already in the process of buying the flat above and owning the whole house.

Where did the money come from? "From wherever it is at that moment." That is a little saying that John and I are always using. I originally heard it from a holy man whose charity was trying to raise money for a special project. It worked for him and it worked for me.

It was like an amazing force which just seemed to align all the favourable situations so that the purchase could be made. I'm still in awe at the way this happened, but what came first was my firm belief it could.

I think intention is a very powerful thing, if you have a strong enough belief you can create anything. Intention won't work on its own. But I don't mean it only works with feng shui. Feng shui is simply the tool directing and focusing intention. Intention needs to be backed with action, a passionate interest, and focus on what you want. Looking back on my old school reports I can see that very clearly in my maths results. I always thought I was very bad at maths. I'd taken the O level twice and failed each time, but when I looked back at my old school reports I was amazed to see that my very first A on those school reports was in maths. Right up until the year before O levels, I did very well at maths not falling below a B. It was only when I got to the year before we took our O levels that I got a C minus. At that time I decided to become a poet, hence losing interest in maths and not putting in the work I clearly needed to do.

To really excel in something, it needs more than just intention. It needs more than just action. It needs you to love it with a passion. Clear intention backed up with action and sprinkled with passion and love can create an incredible life.

What's your body teaching you?

One of the things I noticed as my mother aged was that she used to frequently say, "Oh, I just can't be bothered." I think this mindset was very detrimental to her and could have even contributed to her dementia. I know the death of my brother hit her very hard and I suspect that this didn't help. It could have eventually worn her down.

I am a great believer that our thoughts and emotions have a very profound effect on our physical bodies. When we have health issues, it is a good idea to not only look at the physical causes that may have brought us to ill health, but also check what is going on in our head. Negative thoughts and emotions can also cause disease which can manifest in a physical ailment if the dis-ease is not addressed.

I hope you have looked at what has been happening in your life. Look at the weak areas that always fail when we put too much pressure on ourselves. Maybe we are trying to live up to a standard that we think we have to attain to be the success we think we ought to be.

Are these yours or someone else's standards? A parent's or teacher's? Or even someone else in your life that you think you have to be to live up to their expectations? We often put these unnecessary pressures on ourselves, not realising what we have done or even if they are realistic.

I know not having children has always been a disappointment for me. I always thought that I had to make up for this in some other way. Why? I know this drove me to work harder to make myself as successful as possible, but no matter what I achieved, I did not always give myself the credit I deserved. I realise this now and have slowed down to take better care of myself. Do you need to do this too?

The break in our normal lives that COVID forced upon us has been quite illuminating for many people, including me. We need to learn from every lesson life puts in our way to help us become better human beings so the world can improve and be a kinder, more peaceful place.

The place to start being kind and peaceful is with yourself, in your own body. If that is out of balance, how can we expect to bring balance into the world?

Decade Nine from 80 to 90 years old

WHAT JOY TO MAKE THIS AGE LOOKING AMAZING

Of course I haven't made it to eighty or ninety years old yet, but my wonderful father got to the ripe old age of ninety-four before he passed away. He will be my inspiration for this last decade of this book.

I'm sorry to say, but it's definitely my father's fault that I inherited the skin problems that I've had all these years. My skin certainly took after my father's.

I didn't realise this at first, because my father liked to go in the sun and rarely used any sun protection. I never saw him use any unless it was forced on him by my mother. He agreed reluctantly. Mum would say that he couldn't see his back, but she could see it burning.

Because my father got a bit of a tan and Mum did not, I thought I took after her with my pale untanned skin. It was not until Dad got much older that I realised that he was born with very pale skin, too. He ignored this and it was definitely the reason he ended up with so many sun-related problems as he got older.

My father lived in India for over six years. He was an officer in the Gurkha unit of the army. I'm sure sun protection was not high on the list of priorities there.

Now I know that you don't normally die from skin ailments and diseases, and I know my father didn't die directly because of his skin cancer—but indirectly he definitely did. It was the treatment for a basal cell carcinoma that finished him off. Even though that was not the cause of death listed on his death certificate, it was the straw that broke the camel's back.

He already had quite a few basal cell lesions removed in the past, but this one was more aggressive. It was causing him problems with speaking and eating because it was affecting his jaw and masseter muscle. This was not good for someone who is very sociable and loves his food and drink. It needed to be removed, but he was not able to have an operation because of his age and other health issues. They tried instead to remove it just using a local anaesthetic, but that only removed part of it. It was treated with radiation. My sister and I were very unhappy with this decision, but it wasn't ours to make. Unlike my mother, my father had all his marbles. He had a memory like an elephant. It hardly diminished at all with old age, so he decided to go with what the doctor advised because he was afraid leaving it could make his condition deteriorate.

The radiation treatment was gruelling. To be honest, it made his speech and eating worse. It was miserable for him, but he hung on to the hope that once it was finished, things would get better.

Unfortunately, this was not the case and he had all the side effects of the radiation to deal with, too. This was what my sister and I had been worried about. We had foreseen this, having seen many of our clients also go through this process.

It depressed him, even though he was such a trooper. He rarely complained about being in constant pain and having to drink his G&T through a straw—normally unforgivable for him.

It was so sad to see him give up, eventually having to go on morphine for pain relief. He didn't want to live like that and stopped eating and drinking, having made peace that his life was now coming to an end.

I wonder sometimes if he would have been with us for much longer if he'd not had the radiation therapy for that basal cell carcinoma. But it's a blessing the way things turned out, because we were able to have his funeral at Doncaster Minster with 400 people attending in February 2020.

Just a month later everything got locked down with COVID-19

We thank our lucky stars we didn't have to deal with all the complications that would have come with looking after Dad during that time. He would not have been a good patient with all the restrictions and certainly not wanted to stick to the COVID rules.

My father was well known in the community, but he wasn't famous—infamous would be a better way to describe him. He loved people and having a laugh. I suppose us children are his legacy. I know he did charitable works with his involvement with the Masonic Lodge and was quite high ranking within the society. His main legacy was how he made other people feel. He was always full of fun. He always remembered a person's name and put them at ease with a good joke.

What most impressed me about my father was his wonderful memory. I remember an occasion when we went to a Masonic event where there were over 100 people. My father was getting an award and had to make a speech. Even before he got up to make the speech, people were coming up to greet him. Every single person that approached him, Dad knew their name. He asked men about their wives, knew their names or something about their life. I never saw him falter. It was so impressive to see him converse with all these people, remembering every single part of their lives. He had his full attention on each and every one of them, and no one felt he didn't have time for them

This was a man whose glass was always half-full, and everyone who knew him knew it was a double gin and tonic.

AGEING SKIN CONDITIONS

One thing you have to remember is that a lot of the skin ailments you might get as you age have not had much research done on them because they are more of an inconvenience to us rather than life threatening. Doing research on these conditions costs money and anyone investing in research wants to know they will get a return on their investment. Drug companies or possibly cosmetic companies may decide to do it, but only if they think they can make a product or drug that will give them a profit. This research is very expensive because of all the health and safety measures involved. Rightly so, to keep the consumer safe, but it takes time and lots of trials to check the results so they are taken seriously by the medical profession and government regulators. Most drug companies are not interested because they won't make enough profit from the sale of the medicine or drug, and cosmetic companies have restrictions on how effective the product can be. This is why we speculate on what can cause a condition. When I say we, I mean doctors, dermatologists, and therapists alike. Of course, the longer we see and treat these conditions, the more informed our hypotheses are, but it is based on our experience, not always scientific fact. Only if time and money are invested in these conditions will we get real answers.

One of my clients has a condition called granuloma annulare which is a raised red rash or bumps in a ring pattern on the skin. She usually gets it on her legs, but it is more commonly found on the hands, feet, elbows, and ankles. It's not painful but can sometimes be a bit itchy. It's not known what causes it. There are various theories such as trauma, sun exposure, tuberculosis, and thyroid disease, plus various viral infections. She had typhoid when she was younger and could literally peel her skin off during that time. She even thought it was quite fun to do. I think this was probably the trigger for her granuloma annulare, but it didn't appear till she was in her eighties. It comes and goes, but she is now ninety and still gets it.

Unfortunately, this is what happens with the skin. A trauma or sun exposure can appear to have little or no effect at the time when we are young, but it comes back to haunt us as we age. From eighty to ninety it will definitely rear its ugly head, as it did with my father after all those years with no sun protection. The resulting skin cancer made his life very uncomfortable in those later years.

If you want to have good skin in old age, look after it when you are young. Whatever your age, look after it now.

Skincare for eighties and beyond

Oh, that I reach this age and beyond! Will I still be good with my skincare routines or will I have given up? Will I be too feeble to bother with the basics, too tired to treat myself to a facial? I just don't know. My father had to do so much more for his skin at this age than any other time in his life. Maybe that's because he never did anything else before—no protection of any description—that's probably why it was so bad by the time he got into his nineties.

One thing I discovered over the years is that as we age we seem to need to add more and more things just to keep us feeling alright. We need to exercise more often, sleep more often, rest more often, slow down more often, and drink more often—I mean water. What else could you possibly be thinking of? And some people take medication more often.

I'm afraid skincare follows this pattern. You need to exfoliate more often, moisturise more often, use more anti-ageing products and remember to use them more often, which is not always easy—especially if you are getting age related dementia. So I would say at this age, just do whatever you can, every little bit helps. And bravo to you if you are looking this up for yourself at this age and still give a damn.

Hydration

The thing to remember about hydration is the importance of getting fluids into our bodies, especially as we get to this age.

My poor father nearly died in the hospital, a fate worse than death according to him (now that's a bit of Irish if ever there was!). Seriously, he had taken a turn for the worst. They said he had to go into the hospital—something he was avoiding like the plague. He'd do anything rather than be taken into the hospital—lie, cheat, anything. I think you get the picture here.

He went in with a heart problem, but then he developed an urinary tract infection—very common as you get to this age. It needed to be treated with plenty of hydration, but Dad was not drinking. He was so weak he could not hold the glass to his mouth. Thank goodness I was up from London. When I got to the hospital, I was shocked to see my father looking so bad. The nurse said my father didn't want the water, so I asked if they were administering an IV drip. She said only the doctor could sanction that. I told her to call the doctor immediately.

In the meantime, I encouraged my father to drink. When I put the glass to his mouth, he was happy to drink—with difficulty, but at least the water was going down. I just kept persevering. I dread to think what the outcome would have been if I hadn't been there to administer the water by hand and eventually get the IV drip. My father would not have recovered enough to go back home for the last few more months of his life, eventually dying in his own bed with all the family around him, just the way he wanted to go.

But let me get back on track about the importance of fluids in our bodies. The body is made up mostly of water and our brain needs water to function correctly. The skin looks horrendous if you become dehydrated—think of a dried up prune.

But there are fluids and other fluids. The correct type is very important, but my Dad did very well on G&Ts for most of his life. However, at one stage when we were out in Majorca for a holiday, I had to make him drink at least a glass of water before he could have another G&T. He was getting dehydrated because of the heat.

Tea, coffee, and alcohol are all diuretics which means they make the body flush out water. Many medications can also act as diuretics, so that needs to be taken into account if you are on any pills. If any of these are your preferred tipple, remember you need to drink more water to counteract the diuretic effect. Some other types of commercial drinks have a high sugar content which can cause glycation, a binding of proteins which not only forms wrinkles, but is detrimental to all other parts of the body, too.

I'm sure some of you will be smugly thinking, well I'm drinking lovely delicious fruit juices. These are very healthy, but they also have a downside. They contain fructose which also causes glycation and affects insulin levels, potentially causing Type 2 diabetes. That is not good for our health or our skin and has an impact on weight gain, too. This is why water is always recommended. It has the least amount of negatives associated with it.

If you really can't bear water on its own, try watering down the fruit juice and make sure the juice you choose is not from concentrates which have even higher fructose content than fresh juice.

How can you be authentic?

If I could speak to my nine-year-old self from this wiser, more worldly ninety-year-old person, what would I say?

1. Believe in Yourself

I was told this by my auntie Kathleen when I was in my thirties, but it took at least two decades to realise what she meant and probably another decade to really do it. Would my nine-year-old self take this onboard? Probably not. *What does this old fuddy-duddy know?* I'd probably think to myself. We always think we know better, especially at that age. It's true you need to learn your own lessons in life, but if I had really understood even back in my thirties what this meant and how important it is, I wonder how much more I could have achieved.

If I understood how to believe in myself and listened to my intuition, perhaps I would not have used that awful toner on my skin as a youth, which I believe was part of the slippery slope for my skin problems.

Believing in yourself means trusting your own judgement—that little voice inside that nags at you saying maybe what you are about to do is not a good idea, like having another drink when you know you should really go home. Or it could be you get a hunch that a particular idea is going to be the next big thing, but you don't have the courage, energy, or belief in yourself that brings it into being. Then a few months or years later someone else makes a huge success of the very same thing you thought of.

Has this happened to you? I know the universe has handed me an idea that I have not run with or that I toyed with a bit, then lost faith and gave up, only to see that trend come to fruition a few years later. To be fair, I can be a bit ahead of my time with ideas. They sound wacky to everyone around me, but the one which was to go into the men's grooming market was very sound. It was unheard of back then. Unfortunately, it was before Mr. Beckham made it trendy for men to look after themselves. Someone said you will only get the gays. It was only recently legal to be gay then, so it didn't sound like a great endorsement for a business. We know otherwise now though. It's a wonderful thing in hindsight.

2. Gratitude

You may feel you have nothing, but you have you. Be thankful for this moment in time and that you are here to witness it. There are so many that have perished too young, before they have even begun to contemplate the world. However awful our circumstances are, we have to make the best of them and being grateful for what you have, however little, is the best way to start.

The opposite of gratitude is resentment. This is a horrid negative emotion. You can never see any good in anything if you are resentful of everyone and everything you see. When we are resentful we will not find love, because resentment does not allow love in. And love is the highest emotion to which we should all aspire. Be grateful for your circumstances, however meagre. Let love enter and as we are grateful, we become more open to love. It's amazing how love will do her magic, then our circumstances will get better. It may take a while and you need to practise gratitude daily, but as you get into the habit you will be astonished at the riches it will bring.

I learnt this lesson when I embraced the principles of Sarah Ban Breathnach's book *Simple Abundance: A Daybook of Comfort and Joy*. Her first principle is gratitude. She says that without this, none of the other principles will ever happen. It was not a suggestion, but a must.

Now at this point you may be thinking to yourself, *I thought this was a book about skincare. What does any of this stuff have to do with our skin?* Well, you might have heard of the famous quote from Coco Chanel "Nature gives you the face you have at twenty. Life shapes the face you have at thirty. But at fifty you end up with the face you deserve"

So, although my top two tips appear to have nothing to do with the skin, they certainly are connected if you want your skin to be looking good for the long haul.

Our attitude and how we deal with life makes a huge difference to the skin and where those wrinkles will appear. You might think, *I'll deal with those with Botox and fillers.* Believe me, that is not the way to go. Yes, it may help in the short term, but we both know aged ladies with false-looking faces. In the long run, that is how you will end up if you go down that route. It becomes addictive to try and stay young or keep that perfect youthful skin, but looking after it naturally each day will win out in the end.

I'm not saying you will have a perfect, line-free face at ninety years old. That is not realistic with our lifestyles, the sun altering the DNA of our cells, and the pull of gravity affecting us over time. But your skin will age more gracefully with that sunny attitude you have now acquired from taking onboard the first two tips. They will make you more fun to be with, and that will make you appear far younger than your actual years.

The beauty industry has always been smoke and mirrors. Believe me, it may sound more scientific now, but there is still a lot of smoke and mirrors occurring.

3. Sunsense

It was so tempting to put this as my top tip because the sun is the one sure thing that will age us. It has been proven time and time again. If you keep out of the sun, your skin will look better as you age.

There is no smoke and mirrors going on with the science here. We know for sure that the more sun on the skin, the more aged it will be. If you are unlucky enough to burn your skin, it will not only age worse, but it could turn into one of the different forms of skin cancer which, if not caught in time, could be life threatening. Protect, protect, protect. It's that simple.

4. Be Kind

Being kind is so very important for the whole world. If we were all kind to each other and all the creatures on this earth, how much better the world would be.

But being kind starts with being kind to yourself. If you don't know how to be kind to yourself, then how do you know how to be kind to others?

We have two voices in our heads, one that loves us and wants to take care of us. The other wants to get us into trouble. This voice also likes to beat you up when it thinks you have not been good enough. This voice is the ego. It means well, but it should never be in charge.

It's essential to learn the differences between these two voices when thoughts come into the mind.

Is it the ego guiding us, or is it the kind loving voice which I will call our intuition, but I also see as coming from our heart centre, our God-self or higher power.

I think it was my intuition that guided me when I was very young not to spend time in the sun. I remember thinking it was strange that I didn't want to be with my sister or our friends playing in the sun on the beach. Certainly everyone around me was telling me I was strange, too, but I knew I didn't like being in the sun. It's a pity that peer pressure won out in the end.

5. Simplify Your Skincare and Your Life

Maybe this is something you learn with age, because for the first few decades of my life I think I spent most of my time trying to accumulate things—nothing like a bit of retail therapy to make me smile. I was bad with everything: clothes, shoes, bags, homeware, ornaments, cooking utensils, furniture, you name it! I was especially bad with makeup, skincare, or anything to do with the beauty industry. I just had to have it!

Now I'm far more subdued and discerning. I think the austerity during COVID relieved my need for more. It made me realise that less was best. Also, after clearing out my parents' home, I understood how useless most of the things we buy are. There was so much stuff they owned that had never even been used. It had been stored away for so long that it was useless. For example, someone else couldn't get the benefit on one item because the rubber knobs had deteriorated to such an extent it was unable to work. Uncle George's motto KISS—keep it simple stupid—had never been so apt.

I think we should be very careful when it comes to skincare. "If in doubt leave it out," is another good ditty to remember when you are walking around those cosmetics and skincare aisles at the shopping mall. It's tempting to buy that wonder cream that will take away the wrinkles, but is it right for your skin? I hope after reading this book you will be able to answer that with confidence.

6. Order

When you look in the dictionary, *order* can mean many things. "Keeping things in a particular way, *e.g., she kept her room in an orderly way.* Or a command or instruction, *e.g., you must protect your skin.* Or a request made, e.g. *I will order that product for you today.*" But when I think of order in my life, it is making sure I prioritise the most important things I need to do.

I have learnt my life runs far more smoothly and I get the outcomes I would like when I start my day in an orderly way. I instruct my mind with meditation to stay calm and focused, and I ask for grace to be with me as I conduct my affairs throughout the day.

This morning ritual, of course, includes protection of my skin with my morning skincare routine.

If this all occurs in the order it's supposed to, my day usually goes by in a pleasant agreeable way with some amazing outcomes, whatever life throws at me.

So all these definitions of order have helped me prioritise the day. If the day goes well, there is more chance that the next will, too, and so the week, the year, the life. Maintaining an agreeable amount of order helps maintain a balance, and I'm less likely to go into negative emotions when things don't always go as planned. This is also what we are trying to do with an orderly skincare routine—keeping our skin happy and healthy on a regular basis. When it is happy and healthy, it is more likely to age gracefully and maintain a youthful bloom.

So tip number six is to have an orderly regular skincare routine. But bringing order to your life will also help your skin, because a life that runs smoothly can only help to smooth your skin from getting all those frowns and wrinkles.

7. Happiness is the Greatest Gift We All Possess

I have a wonderful sign on my wall that says, "Happiness is not a destination, it's a way of life." I remember first seeing this sign when I was on holiday with my family in Florida. I just had to get it. We were having a wonderful time, the weather was great, and all was well with the world. Of course, in these circumstances you can easily feel happy, but unfortunately, we can't be on holiday all the time. However I'm really working at trying to make my life feel as if I am.

The words made perfect sense to me. We so often think that certain things have to be in place before we can be happy—this has to happen a certain way or that has to be the end result before we can be happy. But what if you made being happy the way to live your life?

So what do we need to do to take note of those words and make happiness our way of life?

Finding joy in everyday things can help make us feel happy. My bed made in the morning puts a smile on my face because I love seeing the room made up just the way I like it.

Put little things in your day that make you happy. In my case, a cup of coffee just the way I like it always starts the day well. This is a really clever way to balance out the things that can go wrong. Finding something that will spark a bit of joy when the day is not unfolding in exactly the way you would like can redeem what may have turned out to be an awful day.

I call these coping strategies and make sure I have a few little things to keep me smiling.

But there are days when no amount of coping strategies will work, and the day is beyond repair. In these cases, I just decide it's an awful day and there is nothing I can do about it so I may as well resign myself to ending it as soon as possible, so I go to bed early and make plans for a better day tomorrow.

So what's this to do with skin? Don't you think smile lines are much better than frown lines?

8. Beauty

This whole book is about ending up looking and feeling beautiful.

I wish that for us all, but I hope you have realised by now that beauty comes from within. It's not something you can buy in a tube to plaster on your face or have a surgeon rearrange for you.

And beauty is realising you don't need to look beautiful. I know it helps a lot in this western world where we revere youth and beauty above all else. That is such a shame when wisdom and experience are far more valuable.

If you think about those moments in life when you felt most beautiful, I bet you were not in all of them. Hopefully one feels beautiful on one's wedding day, but when the first child was born? Or having achieved something like completing a marathon, was your hair perfect? I think not, but yet you still felt marvellous, on top of the world. I think it's during these special moments when the soul becomes visible that we look our most beautiful.

9. Joy

What a joy to see someone looking healthy and vibrant, who is happy and full of life no matter what their age. Our skin is just one part of the whole of who we are. However good your skin is, if you don't feel that joy of life, you still won't look good. A person can have a face full of wrinkles, but their smile can light up a room. It is as simple as that. Make the joy of life radiate from you and you will look good.

Nine-year-old me, I wish you had known this so many years ago, but it often takes a lifetime to realise how simple life really is.

If you have read this book all the way through rather than just skipped to this last decade, well done. You will have far more of an understanding of the physical and emotional reasons behind the nine tips I have just given you.

If you have just skipped to the back, and I'm well aware of those impatient people who will have done that because I'm one of them, I urge you to at least read through the skin sections of each decade. You will understand how the skin works and the importance of how our whole body, mind, spirit, and emotions affect the outcome of your skin as you age.

Often we live our lives the wrong way round, when we are in that first decade we can't wait to get to the next so that we can make the rules—then break them. We want to grow up too quickly and often pretend we are older than we are.

In our teens we think we know everything and that anyone older than thirty is passed their prime, knows nothing, and is stupid. Also, we think we are invincible—we are never going to get old. I never imagined at that age I would grow old, have wrinkles, and a scraggy neck—that was just not happening to me—but it catches up on us all in the end.

Then in our twenties and thirties we realise it's not that much fun being grown up. Making the rules means being more responsible, and some of us are not quite ready for that. Some of us realise that we grew up far too quickly, and some of us are forced into growing up too soon by parents or circumstances. Growing up is not as great as it was made out to be when we were young. So what should we do instead?

What if we cherished those younger years and didn't try to rush into being older by putting on makeup too soon or making out we are older than our years? What if we learnt from our elders and accepted their wisdom, so we avoided their past mistakes and built on their triumphs? Perhaps then we would move into those later years more prepared, with a more truly earned confidence, rather than the facade most of us use with the smoke and mirrors from the cosmetic industry.

What if we lived life the other way round, keeping youth for the youthful and making the most of that so we don't want or need to hang on to it? Celebrate the years as they go by, knowing that by living life to the full brings lines—and better to have smile lines than frown lines.

Learn to enjoy every minute, each day at a time. Every morning is a brand new day to be cherished and celebrated for the blessing it is. Make the most of it—whatever your age—you are only as old as you feel inside anyway, and as I think you may have gathered from this book, real beauty only comes from within.

Acknowledgments

I have received endless inspiration from my family and friends, clients and colleagues, too numerous to mention each by name, but I would like to thank every single one of you and I am blessed to have you in my life, you know who you are.

Everyone you come into contact with can be a source of inspiration and information.

However the books I have read often speak to me on a very deep level, and the training courses I have attended have taught me a lot and changed me for the better.

Listed are the sources I have learnt from and quoted in this book.

Books

Ban Breathnach, Sarah *Simple Abundance,* Bantom Press, 1996.
Barrett-Hill, Florence *Advanced Skin Analysis,* Virtual Beauty Corporation Ltd, 2004.
Barrett-Hill, Florence *Cosmetic Chemistry,* Virtual Beauty Corporation Ltd, 2009.

AGELESS SKIN FROM NOUGHT TO NINETY

Fitz Patrick Scale from Florence Barrett-Hill, page 67.

Furman RPh, Rachel *Drugs & Cosmetics*, CRF Publications, 2000.

Hay, Louise L *Heal Your Body*, Eden Grove, 1989.

Jeffers, Susan *Feel The Fear And Do It Anyway*, Ballantine Books, 1987.

Jodie Day *Living the Life Unexpected*, Bluebird/PanMacmillan, 2013, revised 2020.

Oxford English Dictionary.

Pugliese MD,Peter T *Physiology of the Skin,* Allured Publishing Corporation, 1996.

Tracy, Brian *Eat That Frog,* Hodder & Stoughton Ltd 2013.

Wilkinson, John et al *Dermatology in focus,* Elsevier Ltd, 2005.

Young, Anne *Practical Cosmetic Science,* Mills & Boon Ltd, 1972.

Other Sources

Capt Tom saying from a BBC One news program.

Gallo RL, Science Inflammation *Propionibacterium Acnes On Our Face,* October 2016.

HandMade Films Python (Monty) *Look on the Bright Side of Life,* Life of Brian, 1979.

NHS www.nhs.uk Seasonal Health, 2020.

NYU Langone Health www.nyulangone.org Types of Rosacea.

Robbins, Tony *Life Mastery Courses, 1998, 2000, 2001.*

Useful Organisations

Aesthetic Medicine.
British Association of Beauty Therapy and Cosmetology BABTAC.
British Beauty Council.
British Institute & Association of Electrolysis.
Comité International D'Esthétique Et De Cosmétologie CIDESCO.
Daoyin Tao Association.
Ellisons Academy.
Guinot Institut de Paris.
Henlow Grange School of Beauty Therapy and Physical Culture.
IIAA International Institute for Anti-Ageing.
Institute of Clinical Aromatherapy.
International Institute of Reflexology.
Pastiche.
Professional Beauty.
The International Dermal Institute.
The Institute for Optimum Nutrition I.O.N.
The Dr Edward Bach Foundation.
NuLife Sciences.
RCN Dermatology Nursing Forum.

Author Bio

Kathleen Birch graduated from the prestigious Champneys Henlow Grange at the top of her class and went on to teach skincare and beauty therapy at the international CIDESCO level. One of her students even went on to become Princess Diana's facialist. Kathleen has worked in the beauty field for clients around the world while with Royal Viking Line, and, for the past thirty years, through her private skincare practice. Most recently, she was in the top five finalists in the Professional Beauty Industry Awards. This is her first book. Kathleen lives in leafy Chiswick, West London, with her husband John and two cats, Bertie and Bella.

URGENT PLEA!

Thank You For Reading My Book!

I really appreciate all of your feedback and
I love hearing what you have to say.

I need your input to make the next version of this
book and my future books better.

Please take two minutes now to leave a helpful review on
Amazon letting me know what you thought of the book:
www.kathleenbirch.com
Thanks so much!

Kathleen

Printed in Great Britain
by Amazon

42695632R00116